# SCOTT BRUCE

# Cereal Boxes & Prizes: 1960s

## A TRIBUTE & PRICE GUIDE

FLAKE WORLD PUBLISHING

BOOK DESIGN BY ELASTIC, CONCORD, MA
PHOTOGRAPHY BY SCOTT BRUCE


PRINTED IN HONG KONG
FIRST PRINTING: MAY 1998
ISBN: 0-9662123-0-4

❖ For Bev, Nick, and Will ❖

## Note on Captions

To avoid run-away captions, sizes, prices, and source credits have been simplified or abbreviated. Here's the key:

**ABBREVIATIONS**: bk(s) = back(s), Can = Canadian, ea = each, and zine = magazine.

**SIZES**: All cereal box and premium sizes refer to height unless otherwise stated. For example, 11" describes a box or toy 11 inches tall. Other dimensions are ignored.

**PRICES**: The cerealectibles market is largely character driven. The more popular the featured 'toon, athlete, or critter on a box, prize or sign, the higher the price the item will command when sold or traded. To paraphrase a real estate mantra, value is determined by "character, character, character."

Rarity also plays an important role in pricing. Demand outweighs supply for most hot-character items, as well as short-lived but indelible sugar-coated brands like Wackies or Kream Krunch, which some collectors would kill for.

Three prices are provided for each item or group of items pictured in this book. These figures correspond to the value of that item (or group of items) in Poor, Very Good, and Mint condition (C2 C6 C10). Group shots are priced with sliding ranges, such as $10-15 $25-45 $35-75 with the least-valued item first and most valuable item last. All values, a consensus of dealer and collector opinion when this book went to press, may be dated after publication.

**COLLECTOR CREDITS**: The uppercase letters in brackets at the end of some captions indicate the source collection(s) of the item(s) pictured. They are, in alphabetical order:

| | |
|---|---|
| AC | Author's collection, Cambridge, MA |
| AS | Aaron Sultan, Raleigh, NC (919) 954 7111 |
| BB | Bill Bruegman, Toy Scouts Inc., Akron, OH (330) 836 0668 |
| BC | Bill Campbell, Birmingham, AL (205) 853 8227 |
| BK | Bob Koenig, Mineola, NY (516) 739 6407 |
| DG/SR | Dan Goodsell & Steve Roden, Tick-Tock Toys, Culver City, CA (310) 815 0465 |
| DG | David Gutterman, Quake Collectibles, Chicago, IL (773) 404 0607 |
| ES | Evan Stuart, Longmont, CO |
| GT | Graham Trievel, West Chester, PA (610) 701 9193 |
| HA | Hake's Americana & Collectibles, York, PA (717) 848 1333 |
| JB | Joseph Biros, Bedford, OH |
| JHC | Johnny Hustle Card Co., Mineola, NY (516) 827 4771 |
| JR | Jim Rash, Egg Harbor Turnpike, NY (609) 646 4125 |
| KM | Kevin Meisner, Freakie Magnet zine, meisner65@aol.com |
| LB | Larry Blodget, Rancho Mirage, CA (760) 862 1979 |
| MB | Mike Blanchard, Cedar Falls, IA (319) 266 6039 |
| RC | Roland Coover, West Chester, PA (610) 692 3112 |
| RP | Ron Prager, Woodhaven, NY |
| RS | Ron Schwinnen, Cresthill, IL (815) 725 0505 |

Unless otherwise noted, all items reproduced in this book belong to the author.

# Acknowledgements

Many dedicated collectors enriched this book by allowing me to photograph their memorabilia in the familiar wallow of my kitchen, backyard and studio. For indulging that creative necessity, my heartfelt thanks go to Roland Coover Jr., Graham Trievel, Aaron Sultan, Larry Blodget, Jim Rash, Ron Schwinnen, Joseph Biros, Mitch Diamond, Bob Koenig, Ron Prager, Don Simonini, Evan Stuart, John Alutto, Steven Roden, and Dan Goodsell. Without their loans, the quality of this book would have been compromised.

I am also deeply grateful to the flake aficionados who, over many years, have heeded my calls and combed the cereal universe for missing pieces to the puzzle. They are—in no particular order—Rocky Flynn, Paul Cozzolino, David Katz, Doug Mark, Bill Bruegman, Ted Hake, Ed Curtis, Virginia and Ralph Moody, Ralph Stout, Mike Blanchard, Brian Munger, Don Phelps, Frank Staley, Jerry Cook, Mike Speth, Darren Wells, Nelson Corey, Tim Krajewski, Bill Otto, Bob Grabosky, Jim Engel, R.H. Bruce, Brett Walters, Gary Miles, Matt Kirscht, Kevin Meisner, Scott Starr, Joe Statkus, Ed Chernesky, David Dowd, David Goldberg, Curt Jones, John Matthews, Mike Paquin, Kirk Holcomb, Mike Frigerio, Chris Orlando, David Gross, Ronnie Salinas, Kelly Jones, Kurt Wolf, Roger Johnson, and Leon Wisser. David Gutterman went out of his way to search, mediate snags, and encourage me when the project hit the wall.

Package illustrator Bob Traverse unleashed the Mother-of-all-Post-Cereal finds, with daughter troves tumbling from Bill Betts and Tom Hollingsworth.

Ed Inglis did a masterful job converting Post wrappers to boxes as well as vetting *Toy Shop* issues for cereal stuff. Mark Fisher drew the *Flake World* logos. Mark Marderosian helped illustrate the cover. Heidi LaFleche and Karen Schlosberg took the text to the woodshed (and returned it much chastened).

Mark Dollins, Denise Zost, and Janet Silverberg of the Quaker Oats Company deserve a big hand for loaning Quisp and Quake to the cause.

Photographic models Nick and Zoe, both first graders, were my secret weapon against boring pictures. Thanks again kids—I know it wasn't Orlando!

Finally, many thanks to Kevin and Jane Grady and Jean Beinart of Elastic Design for pulling off a breathtaking product despite the pinch of short time and an out-of-sight printer. *Love that cover!*

# Corrections

Perfection takes practice. To make sure that the next edition of this book is flawless, please bring any errors or typos you find to my attention. All editorial correspondence should be addressed to:

SCOTT BRUCE
FLAKE WORLD PUBLISHING
PO BOX 481
CAMBRIDGE, MA 02140

TEL (617) 492 5004
FAX (617) 491 8211
EMAIL scottbruce@flake.com

# Author Seeks Rare Cerealectibles

Scott Bruce scours the planet for vintage cereal boxes, prizes, and advertising pieces to complete future and revised editions of his books. With the sequel Cereal Boxes & Prizes: 1970s now in full production, Scott seeks cool '70s stuff, as well as items missing from, or borrowed for, Cereal Box Bonanza: The 1950s, and this '60s volume. For his detailed Want, Trade, and Sales lists, please write, call or email Scott at the above addresses. Thank you.

# Additional Books

Copies of Cereal Boxes & Prizes: 1960s are $29.95 each plus shipping and handling.

Cerealizing America: The Unsweetened Story of American Breakfast Cereal by Scott Bruce and Bill Crawford was hailed by the Chicago Tribune as "a rich blend of enjoyment and nutrition—much like the product itself." Copies of the illustrated 300-page hardback are $29.95 each plus shipping and handling.

Scott Bruce's 212-page book Cereal Box Bonanza: the 1950s sparkles with more than 500 full-color pictures and current market values. Copies of the softcover price guide are $12.95 each plus shipping and handling.

Shipping and handling for any book is $4.50 (add $.75 for each additional copy). Volume discounts for all three books are available.

To order by credit card call toll free 1-888-RU-FLAKE (1-888-783-5253) or order online at www.flake.com. Or send checks or money orders payable to Flake World to:

FLAKE WORLD PUBLISHING
DEPT. K
PO BOX 81363
CHAMBLEE, GA 30366-1363
TEL/FAX (770) 986 8077

# Prologue

Can you name *one* American between the ages of 30 and 50 who doesn't remember begging Mom to "buy me the box with the silly rabbit?"

Or arguing "which tastes better, Quisp or Quake?"

Or screaming "I'm Cuckoo for Cocoa Puffs!" until Dad rolled up the morning newspaper?

Cereal war cries by the score lie buried inside boomer brains like bullets in the sandbags surrounding Ho Chi Minh's Hanoi bunker.

Why? Because Martha Stewart says *we are what we eat*, and more than 30 years ago, *we scarfed down tons of candy-coated cereal*. Twinkles, Lucky Charms, Froot Loops, Wackies, Corn Crackos, Apple Jacks, Honeycomb and Clackers—to name but a few new Trix—shot into supermarkets faster than we could swallow . . . and faster than sweating stock boys could pry open shelf space for.

Driven by breakthroughs in food technology and a few zillion bucks in televised fast talk, an explosion of flake-based creativity rattled the psychedelic '60s. Weird sugary shapes, irresistible "Free Inside" bait, and a parade of animated "grain gods" from Cap 'n Crunch to Lucky the Leprechaun transformed 80 million tots into cereal-sucking zombies. We chanted "I Want My Maypo!," "A Bowl A Day Keeps the Bullies Away!," and "They're GR-R-R-REAT!" until breakfast flew off our spoons . . . and out of our nostrils.

Cerealebrities crowded the decade's advertising landscape in every guise, from baseball players and rock stars to a small-town sheriff and his bumbling deputy. Even Yogi Bear, Huckleberry Hound, and Rocky and Bullwinkle were hired to shovel flakes into our tiny, upturned mouths. One grain-god ghetto commanded such weekly devotion from boomers that some church and school officials cried foul. "You might say we invented Saturday morning," boasted one Battle Creek mogul to *Fortune* magazine.

Scott Bruce and Bill Crawford

(To understand how the cereal biz morphed from a handful of 19th-century health nuts into a multi-billion-dollar industry, read the critically acclaimed book *Cerealizing America: The Unsweetened Story of American Breakfast Cereal*. You'll never sniff a corn flake the same way again! Ordering information on page 8).

So what happened to the B-52 loads of day-glo packets and toy whatchamacallits that, along with the TV commercials, bombed us into the involuntary cereal savants we are today?

GET THE HILARIOUS SCOOP ON ROCKY & BULLWINKLE, YOGI BEAR, QUISP & QUAKE, FRANKEN BERRY, FREAKIES, AND OTHER BREAKFAST FAVORITES IN *CEREALIZING AMERICA: THE UNSWEETENED STORY OF AMERICAN BREAKFAST CEREAL*. SEE ORDERING INFO ON PAGE 8.

You know, all the cool collectible stuff that once had us firmly by the bowls?

Flung into dumpsters by vengeful stock boys, store displays were the first to disappear. Cereal packages were burned in backyard blazes on top of dad's *Playboys*. Plastic gizmos, dug out of the box or mailed away for, were heaved after little Joey choked on an Archie car wheel, Batman ring, or Seadog bo'sun whistle. Hoover-wielding Moms fed whatever escaped these purges to the holocaust of Spring Cleaning.

Leaving only, it seems, a nest of "magically delicious" sound bites wriggling inside our soggy, middle-aged cortexes. After watching *Nick At Nite* are you nagged by the jingle "like a chocolate milkshake only crunchy"? When you reminisce about a rotor-tailed orange elephant, do your kids bite their lips and look away? Ever salivate for the taste of "little sugar-coated donuts" but can't recall the *!!#&❊#❊@!!* brand name? *Doggone it! . . . What was* "the one and only cereal that comes in the shape of animals"?

At last, there is a cure for the scourge of Cerealopathy.

With relics plucked from dusty pantries, manufacturers' trash heaps, and Battle Creek flea markets, Cereal Boxes & Prizes: 1960s thumbs its proverbial nose at the nation's waste-disposal system to reveal the ancient-but-oh-so-familiar topography of our cereal-soaked childhood. Year by year, Rice Krispies by Rice Krinkles, from Camelot to the Moon Landing, nearly every box and toy we once screeched for 'til Mom's skirt was in shreds and her ears bled leaps miraculously out of this breakfast bible in vibrant, mouth-watering color.

WOW!

Quisp and Quake DID wrangle like doves and hawks during the Vietnam War! Andy Griffith WAS on the box of Grape Nuts Flakes! Monkees flicker rings WERE from Puffa Puffa Rice, not gumball machines! The freeze-dried disks in Corn Flakes with Instant Bananas DO look like communion wafers (and melted down to disgusting goo)! A lift in the Beatles' Yellow Submarine DIDN'T stop Nabisco Honeys from sinking beneath the waves! And Linus the Lionhearted first stampeded Crispy Critters down the linoleum in 1962, not 1965, as your know-it-all neighbor swears! Yes. YES!

*You aren't quazy after all!*

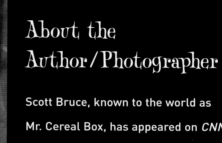

## About the Author / Photographer

Scott Bruce, known to the world as
Mr. Cereal Box, has appeared on *CNN*,
*CBS Morning News*, *Entertainment
Tonight*, and the *Today* show talking
about cereal.  His other books include
*Cerealizing America: The Unsweetened
Story of American Breakfast Cereal*
(with Bill Crawford), *Cereal Box Bonanza:
The 1950s*, and *Lunch Box: The Fifties and
Sixties*.  Scott uploads his prize-winning
*Flake World* web site (www.flake.com)
from Cambridge, Massachusetts.

Howdy Doody rings—WHEAT HONEYS
9.5". NABISCO. 1960.   $100 $150 $200

Howdy Doody rings—WHEAT HONEYS (bk)
9.5", NABISCO, 1960. $100 $150 $200

Howdy Doody rings
EA .75" ACROSS, NABISCO, 1960. EA $15 $20 $25 [RC]

Indian wars medal—WHEAT HONEYS
9", NABISCO, 1960. $50 $75 $100

Frontier hero medal—RICE HONEYS
9", NABISCO, 1960. $50 $75 $100

Frontier hero & Indian war medals
4" LONG, NABISCO, 1960. EA $5 $7 $10

Corvair contest/Impala Model—TRIX
9.5", GENERAL MILLS. 1960. $100 $125 $150

Corvair contest/Impala Model—TRIX (bk)
9.5", GENERAL MILLS. 1960. $100 $125 $150

1960 Impala Model
8" LONG. GENERAL MILLS. 1960. $75 $125 $175

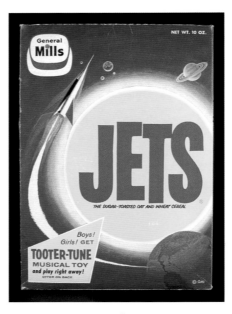

Tooter-tune toy--JETS
9.5". GENERAL MILLS. 1960. $75 $125 $150

Fruit offer—RICE KRISPIES, Fruit offer—CORN FLAKES (Can),
& Ford contest—CORN FLAKES (bks)
8.5"/12.5"/9.75". KELLOGG. 1960. $25-35 $50-65 $75-95

Fruit Offer–RICE KRISPIES, Woody Woodpecker comic strip– RAISIN BRAN,
& Ford contest–CORN FLAKES

KELLOGG, 1960.

Woody Woodpecker comic strip–RAISIN BRAN
9.5", GENERAL MILLS, 1960. $75 $100 $125

Huckleberry Hound TV show album (store item)
12.5" X 12.5". KELLOGG. 1960. $15 $25 $45

Huckleberry Hound toy statues
1.5"-2". KELLOGG. 1959-60. EA $15-25 [RC]

Catapult game (Big Otis)—OKs
11.25". KELLOGG. 1960. $125 $175 $225

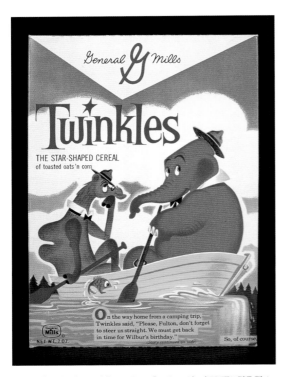

Storybook (Twinkles the elephant)—TWINKLES
9.5", GENERAL MILLS, 1960.  $200 $300 $400

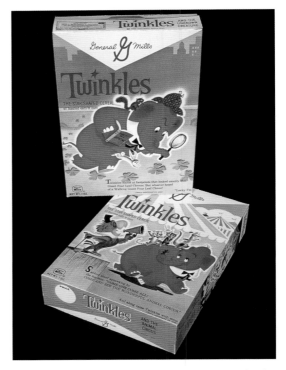

Storybook (Twinkles the elephant)—TWINKLES
EA 9.5", GENERAL MILLS, 1960.  EA $200 $300 $400

Storybook (Twinkles the elephant)—TWINKLES (bks)
EA 9.5", GENERAL MILLS, 1960.  EA $200 $300 $400

Twinkles the elephant bank (store item)
9.5" LONG. GENERAL MILLS. 1960. $200 $350 $500

Twinkles the elephant sponge
4.25" X 3.25". GENERAL MILLS. 1960-61. $10 $25 $50

Twinkles the elephant costume (store item)
GENERAL MILLS. 1960. $75 $100 $125 [RC]

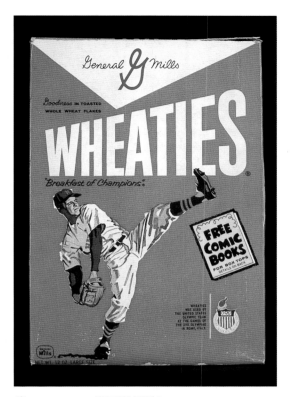

Classic comics—WHEATIES
10.75", GENERAL MILLS, 1960.  $100 $125 $150

Classic Comics—WHEATIES (bk)
10.75", GENERAL MILLS, 1960.  $100 $125 $150

Classic illustrated junior comics
10" X 7", GENERAL MILLS. 1960.  EA $3 $7 $15 [RP]

Million dollar contest
(Johnny Jet)—JETS
9.5". GENERAL MILLS. 1960.
$150 $175 $200

Million dollar contest—TRIX
9.5". GENERAL MILLS. 1960.
$150 $200 $250

Million dollar contest—
CORN KIX
9.5". GENERAL MILLS. 1960.
$75 $100 $125

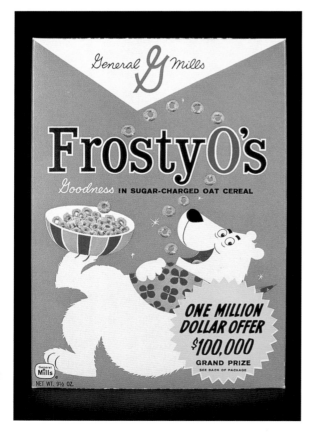

Million dollar contest (Frosty Bear)—FROSTYO's
9.5". GENERAL MILLS. 1960.
$175 $225 $275

Frosty Bear costume (store item)
GENERAL MILLS. 1960. $75 $100 $150 [RC]

Sherman & Peabody wiggle picture (1 of 6 from WHEAT HEARTS)
1" X 1.25", GENERAL MILLS, 1960. $5 $10 $15

FROSTYO's & (rag doll rabbit) TRIX singles
EA 4", GENERAL MILLS, 1960-66. EA $25 $50 $75

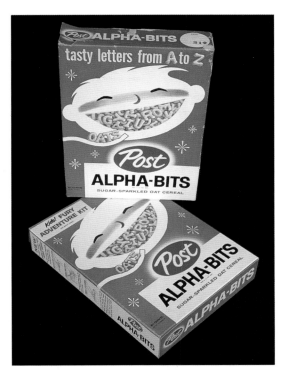

Ruff and Reddy cutout & Fury adventure kit— ALPHA BITS
POST, 1960.

Fury adventure kit—ALPHA BITS (bk)
8.5", POST, 1960. $100 $150 $200

Fury adventure kit
4.25", POST, 1960.  $75 $125 $175

Ruff and Reddy cutout—ALPHA BITS (bk)
8.5", POST, 1960.  $100 $150 $200

Assembled Ruff and Reddy cutout
7" X 5", POST, 1960.  $7 $15 $25

Introductory (three sheep)–TOP 3
10". POST. 1960. $75 $100 $125

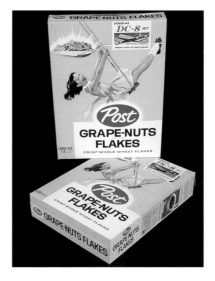

Modern jet liner models–GRAPE NUTS FLAKES
10"/11.5" TALL. POST. 1960.

Modern jet liner models—GRAPE NUTS FLAKES (bks)
POST. 1960. EA $75 $100 $125

Russian Tu-104 jet model
8.5" LONG. POST. 1960. $25 $45 $60

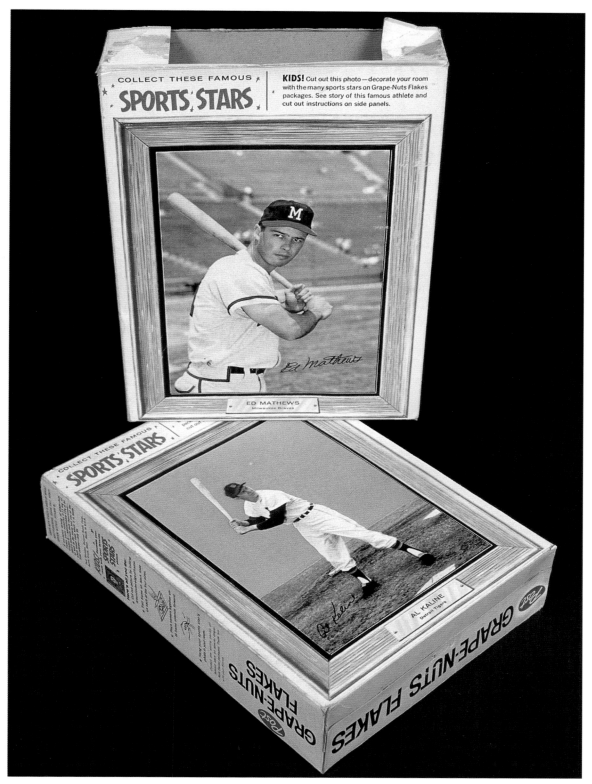

Sports stars (swinging girl)–GRAPE NUTS FLAKES (bks)
EA 10". POST. 1960. EA $250 $400 $500 [JHC]

Mickey Mantle sports stars card (cutout)
POST. 1960. $500 $750 $1,000 [JHC]

Plymouth Fury–TOASTIES, RAISIN BRAN,
& 40% BRAN FLAKES
POST. 1960.

Plymouth Fury–40% BRAN FLAKES (bk)
11". POST. 1960. $75 $100 $125

Plymouth station wagon model
8.25" LONG. POST. 1960.  $75 $125 $150

Plymouth (So-Hi)–KRINKLES
9.75", POST, 1960. $75 $100 $125

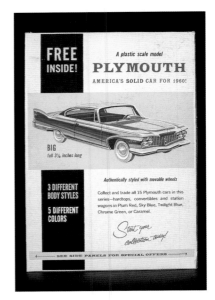

Plymouth (So-Hi)–KRINKLES (bk)
POST, 1960. $75 $100 $125

Plymouth scale models
3.2" LONG, POST, 1960. EA $10 $15 $20 [LB]

Handy & Dandy bears mug & bowl set—SUGAR CRISP
9.75", POST, 1960. $75 $100 $125

Handy & Dandy bears mug & bowl
STACK 5.5", POST, 1960. SET $25 $50 $75

Handy & Dandy bears drum milk pitcher
5.75" ACROSS, POST, 1960. $25 $50 $75 [RC]

SUGAR COATED CORN FLAKES & KRINKLES singles on a POST-TENS zine ad
SINGLES EA 4", $10 $25 $45. AD 13.5" X 21", $5 $7 $10. POST, 1960

Walking finger puppet (Wizard of Oats)—ALL STARS
9.75". KELLOGG. 1960. $100 $125 $150

Huck Hound show cartoon cutouts—
ALL STARS (bks)
EA 9.75", KELLOGG, 1960. EA $100 $125 $150

Huck Hound membership club, Huck Hound fun
masks, & Yogi mug & Huck bowl—CORN FLAKES
KELLOGG, 1960.

Huck Hound fun masks (Mr. Jinx & Big Otis)—CORN FLAKES (bks)
11.5"/9.75", KELLOGG, 1960. EA $75 $100 $125

Mr. Jinx mask, Huck Hound finger puppet, & Huck Hound action cutout
6.5"-7.25". KELLOGG. 1960. EA $5 $10 $15

Huck Hound club—CORN FLAKES (bk)
9.75", KELLOGG, 1960.  $75 $100 $125

Huck Hound club kit
MAILER 8.5" X 11.5", KELLOGG, 1960.
$75 $100 $150 [DG/SR]

Yogi mug & Huck bowl—
CORN FLAKES (bk)
12.5", CAN KELLOGG, 1960.  $100 $125 $150

Yogi Bear mug & Huck Hound bowl
STACK 5.75", KELLOGG, 1960.  SET $15 $25 $40

Yogi & Huck spoons, Yogi stuffed
toys—RICE KRISPIES
EA 10.25", CAN KELLOGG, 1960.

Yogi & Huck spoons—RICE KRISPIES (bk)
10.25", CAN KELLOGG, 1960.  $75 $100 $125

Yogi & Huck stuffed toys—
RICE KRISPIES (bk)
10.25", CAN KELLOGG, 1960.
$100 $150 $200

Yogi & Huck spoons
EA 6" LONG, KELLOGG, 1960.  EA $5 $10 $15

Yogi's movin' pictures (Big Otis)—OKs
11.5". KELLOGG. 1960.  $150 $200 $250

Recipe (Coco the elephant)—COCOA KRISPIES
9.75". KELLOGG. 1960.  $100 $125 $150

Yogi & Huck stuffed toys
17"-18". KELLOGG. 1960.  EA $15 $25 $45

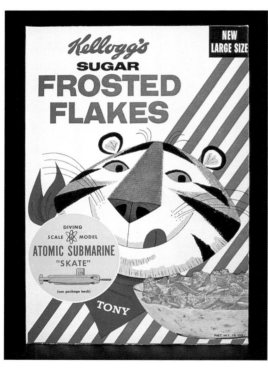

U.S.S. Skate model—FROSTED FLAKES
11.5", KELLOGG, 1960. $75 $100 $125

U.S.S. Skate model—FROSTED FLAKES (bk)
11.5", KELLOGG, 1960. $75 $100 $125

Color-by-numbers (Smaxey Seal)—SUGAR SMACKS
9.75", KELLOGG, 1960.  $75 $100 $125

SMACKS & POPS singles on (Jay North)
RICE KRISPIES zine ad
SINGLES EA 4".  $10 $20 $35
AD 13.5" X 10.5", $5 $7 $10, KELLOGG, 1960.

Jolly clown breakfast buddy & speedy spaceman—RICE HONEYS
EA 9.5", NABISCO, 1961. EA $75 $100 $125

Buffalo Bee breakfast buddy & racing robot—WHEAT HONEYS
EA 9.5", NABISCO, 1961.  EA $75 $100 $125

Buffalo Bee & jolly clown breakfast buddies—HONEYS (bks)
EA 9.5", NABISCO, 1961.  EA $75 $100 $125

Buffalo Bee & jolly clown breakfast buddies
EA 2.25". NABISCO. 1961.  $5 $7 $10

Racing robot & speedy spaceman—HONEYS (bks)
EA 9.5". NABISCO. 1961.  EA $75 $100 $125

Totem pole head—SPOON SIZE
SHREDDED WHEAT
7.75". NABISCO. 1961.  $25 $45 $65

Racing robot & speeding spaceman
EA 2". NABISCO. 1961.  EA $7 $15 $25

"I Want My Maypo!" window banner
24" X 37". MALTEX. 1961. $200 $300 $400

Marky Maypo shirt offer—MAYPO
7", MALTEX, 1961. $100 $150 $200

Marky Maypo cereal set side panel
2" WIDE, MALTEX, 1961. $5 $7 $10

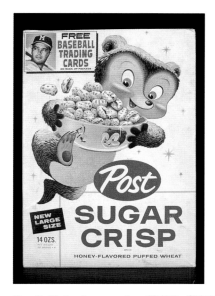

Baseball trading cards–SUGAR CRISP
11", POST, 1961.  $100-125 $175-250 $250-350

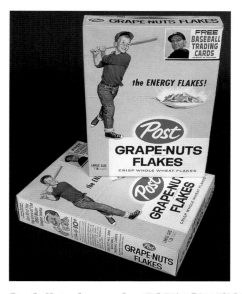

Baseball trading cards–GRAPE NUTS FLAKES
11", POST, 1961.  EA $100-125 $175-250 $250-350 [JHC]

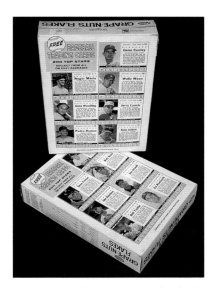

Baseball trading cards–GRAPE NUTS FLAKES (bks)
11", POST, 1961.  EA $100-125 $175-250 $250-350 [JHC]

Marky Maypo cereal set (figure & bowl)
9", MALTEX, 1961.  $50 $75 $100

Baseball trading cards sales brochure
COVER 10" X 12". POST. 1961. $75 $100 $125

Baseball trading cards sales brochure
COVER 10" X 12". POST. 1961. $75 $100 $125

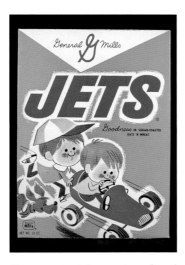

Picnic cutout (go-carting boys)—JETS
9.5", GENERAL MILLS, 1961.  $75 $100 $125

Nestle's Quik (puppet rabbit)—TRIX
9.5", GENERAL MILLS, 1961.  $100 $150 $200

King Leonardo mask—CHEERIOS
12.25", GENERAL MILLS, 1961.  $50 $75 $100

King Leonardo mask—CHEERIOS (bk)
12.25", GENERAL MILLS, 1961.  $50 $75 $100

Train station (Cocoa Puff Kids)—COCOA PUFFS
9.5". GENERAL MILLS. 1961. $150 $200 $250

Train station Cocoa Puffs (bk)—COCOA PUFFS
9.5". GENERAL MILLS. 1961. $150 $200 $250

Cocoa Puff Kids train station & King Leonardo mask
STATION 30". GENERAL MILLS. 1961.  $75 $100 $125

Cocoa Puff Kids crazy train
12" LONG. GENERAL MILLS. 1959-61.  $50 $75 $100

Bugs Bunny game boxes (bks)
POST, 1961.  EA $50 $75 $100

Bugs Bunny game—ALPHA BITS
10". POST, 1961.  $50 $75 $100

Bugs Bunny magic picture (So-Hi)—
RICE KRINKLES
9.75". POST, 1961.  $75 $100 $125

Bugs Bunny magic picture boxes (bks)

POST, 1961. EA $75 $100 $125

Bugs Bunny post cards—RAISIN BRAN

9.75", POST, 1961. $50 $75 $100

Bugs Bunny post card boxes—
RAISIN BRAN (bks)

9.75", POST, 1961. EA $50 $75 $100

Magic water paint book (Cornelius)—
SUGAR COATED CORN FLAKES
11", POST, 1961.  $100 $125 $150

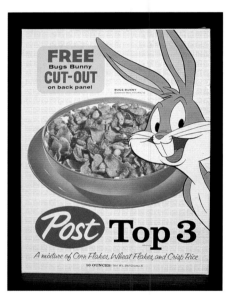

Bugs Bunny cutouts (Bugs Bunny)—TOP 3
10", POST, 1961.  $100 $150 $200

Magic water paint book—
SUGAR COATED CORN FLAKES (bk)
& Magic water paint book
11.25" X 8.5", POST, 1961.  $25 $50 $75 [AC/DG/SR]

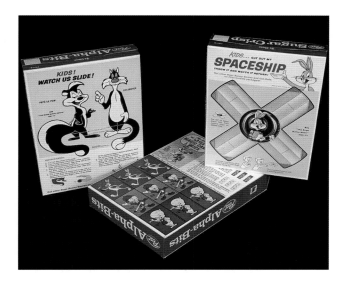

Bugs Bunny cutouts boxes (bks)
POST, 1961. EA $50 $75 $100

Bugs Bunny mask boxes
POST, 1961. EA $75 $100 $125

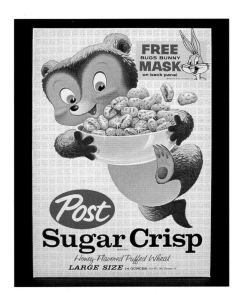

Bugs Bunny mask (Dandy bear)—SUGAR CRISP
11.25". POST, 1961. $75 $100 $125

Porky Pig, Bugs Bunny, & Elmer Fudd cutout masks
7.5"-11". POST. 1961.  EA $3 $7 $10

Singles on magic water picture POST-TENS trays (flats)
SINGLES EA 4", POST, 1961.  EA $15 $20 $25
TRAYS 5.5" X 16.5", POST, 1961.  EA $25 $50 $75

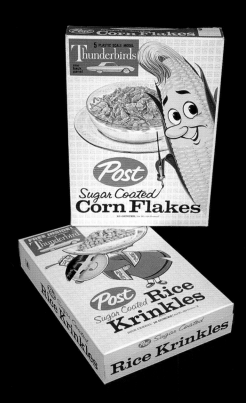

Thunderbird model—SUGAR COATED
CORN FLAKES & RICE KRINKLES
11"/9.75", POST, 1961.  EA $75 $100 $125

Thunderbird model—SUGAR COATED
CORN FLAKES & RICE KRINKLES (bks)
11"/9.75", POST, 1961.  EA $75 $100 $125

1961 Thunderbird scale models
EA 3.2" LONG. POST. 1961. EA $10 $15 $20 [LB]

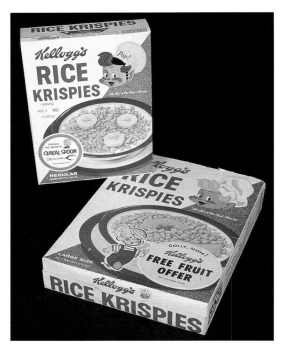

Dennis the Menace cereal spoon & free fruit offer—
RICE KRISPIES

KELLOGG, 1961.

Dennis the Menace cereal spoon (Pop)—
RICE KRISPIES (bk)

8.5", KELLOGG, 1961.  $75 $100 $125

Switch faces—SHREDDED WHEAT, 3–D
laughing face—RAISIN BRAN, & Huck Hound
stampets printing set—CORN FLAKES

KELLOGG, 1961.

Switch faces—SHREDDED WHEAT & two 3–D
laughing face—RAISIN BRAN (bks)

7.75"/8.5"/9.75", KELLOGG, 1961.  EA $25 $50 $75

Huck Hound stampets printing set.
CASE 4.5" LONG, KELLOGG, 1961. $15 $25 $45

Huck Hound stampets printing set—
CORN FLAKES (bk)
11.5", KELLOGG, 1961. $75 $100 $125

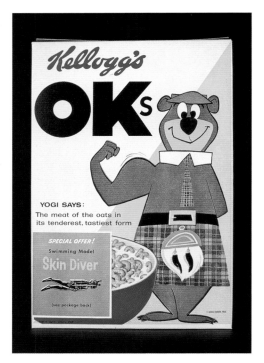

Skin diver model (Yogi in kilt)—OKs
11.5". KELLOGG. 1961. $100 $200 $300

Skin diver model (Yogi in kilt)—OKs (bk)
11.5". KELLOGG. 1961. $100 $200 $300

Nautilus model (Wizard of Oats)—
ALL STARS (bk)
9.75". KELLOGG. 1961. $100 $125 $150

U.S.S. Nautilus model
4.5" LONG. KELLOGG. 1961. $25 $50 $75

Nautilus model (Wizard of Oats)—
ALL STARS
9.75". KELLOGG. 1961. $100 $125 $150

Mark Wilson's trick (Sugar Pops
Pete)—SUGAR POPS
9.75", KELLOGG, 1961. $75 $100 $125

Mark Wilson's trick
(Snagglepuss)—COCOA KRISPIES
9.75", KELLOGG, 1961.
$150 $250 $350

Mark Wilson's trick
(Huck Hound)—ALL STARS
9.75", KELLOGG, 1961.
$200 $350 $500

Mark Wilson's trick (Quick Draw
McGraw)—SUGAR SMACKS
9.75", KELLOGG, 1961. $150 $250 $350

Mark Wilson's mystery trick boxes (bks)
KELLOGG, 1961.

Boo Boo TRIPLE SNACK & SUGAR POPS singles on zine ad
SINGLES EA 4", KELLOGG, 1961.
$35 $50 $75/$10 $15 $30
AD 13.5" X 10.5", KELLOGG, 1961. $5 $10 $15

Shari Lewis finger puppets—LIFE
& sales brochure
QUAKER OATS, 1962.

Shari Lewis finger puppets—LIFE (bk)
9.5". QUAKER OATS, 1962.  $75 $100 $125

Shari Lewis finger puppets
EA 2", QUAKER OATS, 1962. EA $10 $15 $25 [JR]

962

Lamb Chop & Hush Puppy hand puppets
EA 7.5", QUAKER OATS, 1962. EA $15 $25 $45

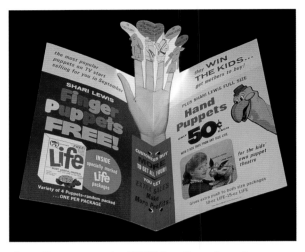

Shari Lewis puppets—LIFE brochure (open)
COVER 11" X 8.5", QUAKER OATS, 1962. $35 $60 $100

Lark Daytona model—CHEERIOS
9.5", GENERAL MILLS, 1962. $100 $125 $150

Lark Daytona model—CHEERIOS (bk)
9.5", GENERAL MILLS, 1962. $100 $125 $150

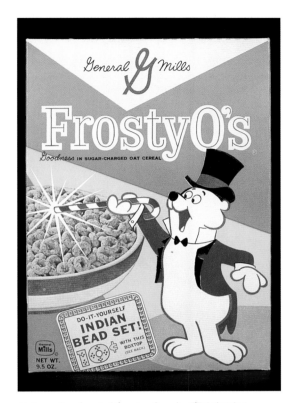

Indian bead set (Frosty Bear)—FROSTYO'S
9.5", GENERAL MILLS, 1962.  EA $100 $150 $200

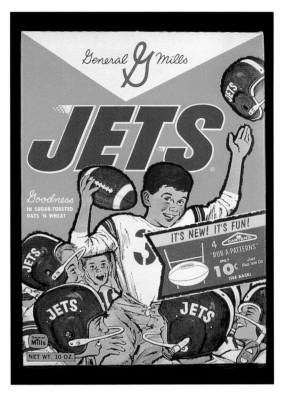

Rub-a-patterns (football kids)—JETS
9.5", GENERAL MILLS, 1962.  $50 $75 $100

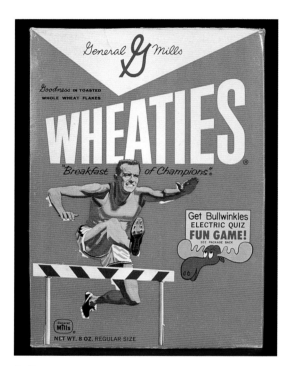

Bullwinkle quiz game—WHEATIES
9.5". GENERAL MILLS, 1962. $100 $150 $200

Bullwinkle quiz game—WHEATIES (bk)
9.5". GENERAL MILLS, 1962. $100 $150 $200

Bullwinkle electric quiz game
11" X 11", GENERAL MILLS, 1962.  $35 $50 $75

Bob Richards' "Take Five" album
10.25" X 10.25", GENERAL MILLS, 1962.  $15 $25 $35

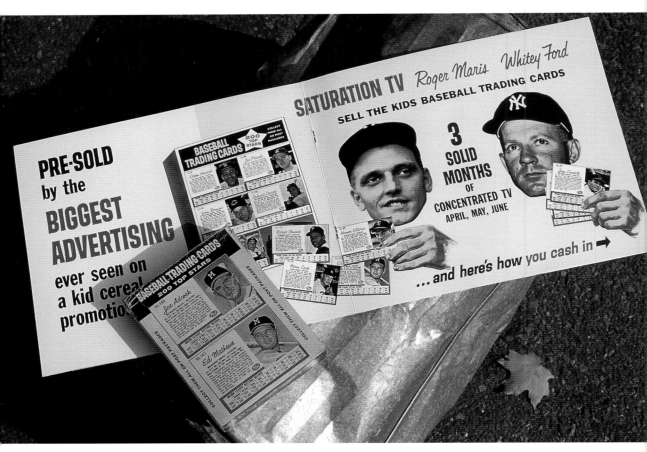

Baseball card sales brochure & Adcock/Matthews cards—GRAPE NUTS (bk)
BROCHURE COVER 10" X 12"
BOX 6.25", POST, 1962.  $75-100 $100-125 $125-150

Baseball cards—TOASTIES & KRINKLES
11.75"/9.5", POST, 1962. $75-100 $125-150 $175-200 [JHC]

Baseball cards—TOASTIES
& KRINKLES (bks)
11.75"/9.5", POST, 1962.
$75-100 $125-150 $175-200 [JHC]

Maris, Mays, Clemente, & Mantle baseball cards (cutouts)
EA 2.5" X 3.5", POST, 1962. $5-50 $10-75 $15-100 [JHC]

Astronaut book—COUNT OFF
9.5", POST, 1962. $100 $150 $200

Astronaut book—COUNT OFF (bk)
9.5", POST, 1962. $100 $150 $200

SUGAR CRISP & KRINKLES singles
EA 4", POST, 1962. $10 $20 $30

Football cards—CRISPY CRITTERS
9.5", POST, 1962. $175 $225 $350

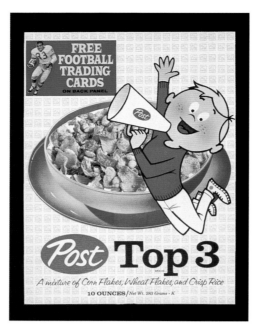

Football cards (cheerleader boy)—TOP 3 (front panel)
POST. 1962. $5 $10 $15

Football cards—TOASTIES, GRAPE NUTS, 40% BRAN FLAKES, & sales brochure
12"/8"/9.5". POST. 1962. $150-350 $175-375 $200-450

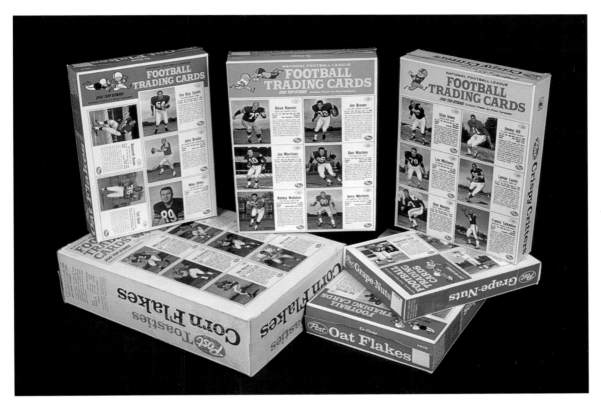

Assorted football trading card boxes (bks)

POST. 1962.  $150-350 $175-375 $200-450

"Touchdown!" football trading cards sales brochure
COVER 10" X 12". POST, 1962. $50 $75 $100

Yogi head masks, Dennis the Menace mug,
Yogi game cloth, & pin-me-ups—CORN FLAKES
KELLOGG, 1962.

Yogi game cloth—CORN FLAKES (bk)
9.75". KELLOGG, 1962. $75 $100 $125

Yogi head mask—CORN FLAKES (bk)
12.5". CAN KELLOGG, 1962. $75 $100 $125

Yogi Bear game cloth
36" X 44", KELLOGG, 1962. $25 $45 $65

Dennis the Menace mug & bowl—
CORN FLAKES (bk)
9.75", KELLOGG, 1962. $75 $100 $125

Dennis the Menace mug & bowl
STACKED 5.5", KELLOGG, 1962. SET $15 $30 $50

Pin-me-ups (Yogi Bear)—OKs
10.25", KELLOGG, 1962. $100 $200 $300

Huck Hound, Doggie Daddy, & Quick Draw McGraw
pin-me-up boxes (bks)
11.5"/9.5"/10.25", KELLOGG, 1962. $35-100 $65-200 $75-300

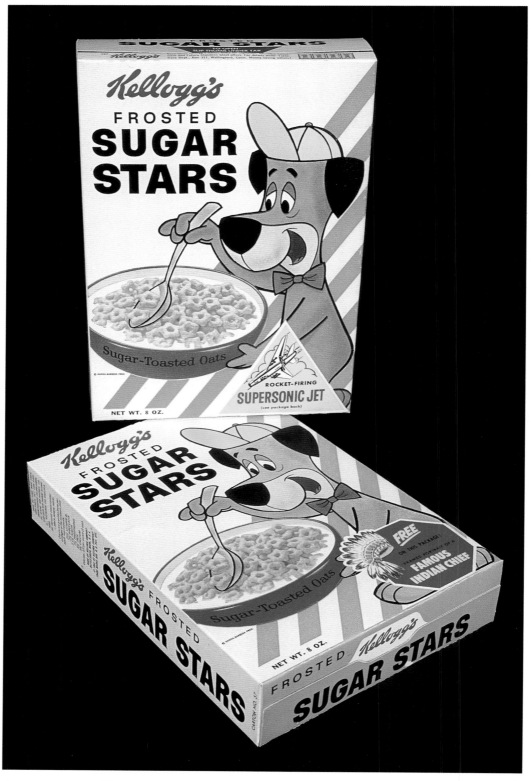

Supersonic jet model & famous Indian chief (Huck Hound)—SUGAR STARS
KELLOGG. 1962. EA $200 $350 $500

Supersonic jet model—SUGAR STARS (bk)
9.75". KELLOGG. 1962. $200 $350 $500

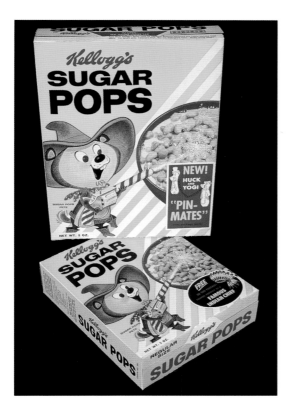

Huck & Yogi pin-mates & famous Indian chief
(Sugar Pops Pete)—SUGAR POPS
KELLOGG. 1962. EA $75 $125 $150

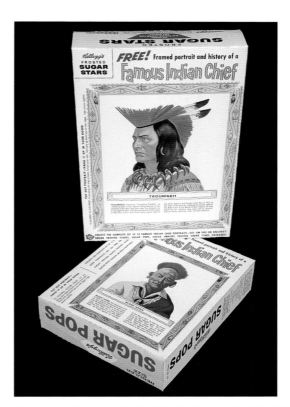

Famous Indian chief—SUGAR STARS & SUGAR POPS
7.25"/9.75". KELLOGG. 1962. $75-200 $125-350 $150-500

Huck & Yogi pin-mates—SUGAR POPS (bk)
9.75", KELLOGG, 1962.  $75 $100 $125

Huck & Yogi pin-mates
EA 1.75", KELLOGG, 1962.  $25 $50 $75

Yogi birthday comic—CORN FLAKES
11.5". KELLOGG. 1962. $200 $300 $500

Yogi birthday comic—CORN FLAKES (bk)
11.5", KELLOGG, 1962. $200 $300 $500

Yogi birthday party comic
10.25" X 7.25", KELLOGG, 1962. $10 $25 $35

Quick Draw SMACKS & Huck Hound STARS
singles on zine ad
SINGLES EA 4", KELLOGG, 1962. EA $15 $25 $50
AD 13.5" X 10.5", KELLOGG, 1962. $5 $10 $15

Yogi's "late-late special" CORN FLAKES counter display
17" X 13" X 2", KELLOGG, 1962.  $200 $300 $400

Comic books—CAP'N CRUNCH
9.5", QUAKER OATS, 1963. $100 $175 $250

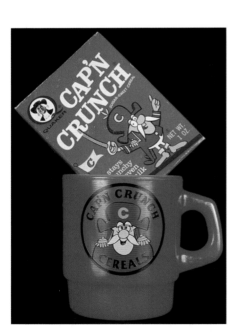

Cap'n mug (corp. gift) & CAP'N CRUNCH sample
3.75", QUAKER OATS, 1963. $10-100 $15-175 $25-250

Comic books—CAP'N CRUNCH (bk)
9.5", QUAKER OATS, 1963. $100 $175 $250

Cap'n Crunch comic books
2.5" X 6.5", QUAKER OATS, 1963. $10 $20 $35 [RC]

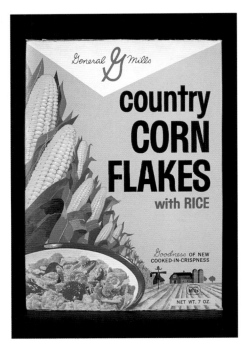

COUNTRY CORN FLAKES
9.5", GENERAL MILLS, 1963. $15 $30 $45

COUNTRY CORN FLAKES (bk)
9.5", GENERAL MILLS, 1963. $15 $30 $45

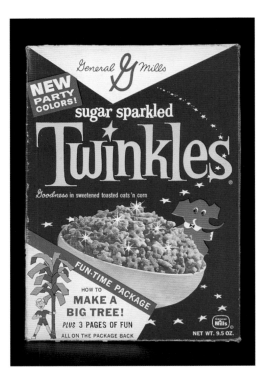

Grab-bag flap—TWINKLES
9.5", GENERAL MILLS, 1963. $75 $125 $175

Grab-bag flap—TWINKLES (bk)
9.5", GENERAL MILLS, 1963. $75 $125 $175

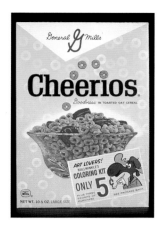

**Bullwinkle coloring kit—CHEERIOS**
11", GENERAL MILLS, 1963. $100 $150 $200

**Bullwinkle coloring kit—CHEERIOS (bk)**
11", GENERAL MILLS, 1963. $100 $150 $200

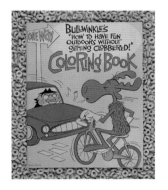

**Bullwinkle coloring book (no crayons)**
11" X 8.5", GENERAL MILLS, 1963. $15 $30 $45

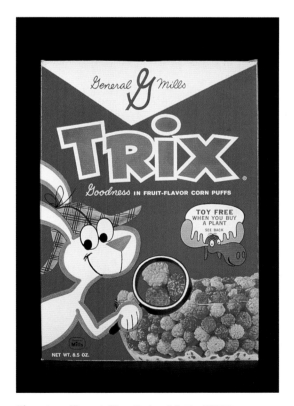

**Free toy (deerstalker hat rabbit)—TRIX**
9.5", GENERAL MILLS, 1963. $100 $150 $200

Don Drysdale baseball card (two sided) over-aisle sign (folds & center cut)
26.5" X 32.5". POST. 1963. $100 $350 $500 [JHC]

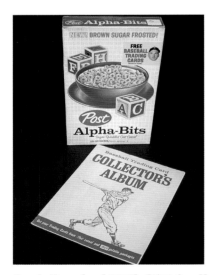

Baseball cards—ALPHA BITS & collector's album
ALBUM 10.5" X 8.75". POST. 1963. $50 $75 $100 [JHC]

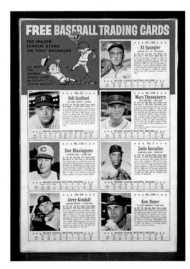

Baseball cards—ALPHA BITS (bk)
11.75". POST. 1963. $75 $125 $175 [JHC]

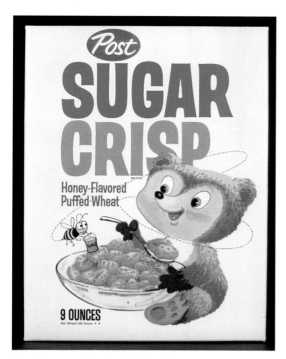

(Dandy-type bear)—SUGAR CRISP
9.5", POST, 1963.  $45 $75 $95

Cowboys & Indians (Jack E. Leonard Postman)—
ALPHA BITS
9.5", POST, 1963.  $125 $150 $175

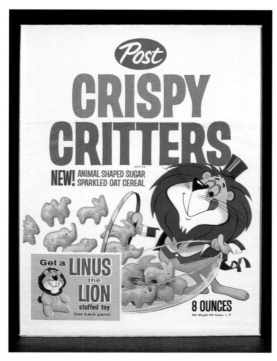

Linus the Lion stuffed toy—CRISPY CRITTERS
9.75", POST, 1963.  $100 $200 $300

Linus the Lion stuffed toy—CRISPY CRITTERS (bk)
9.75". POST. 1963. $100 $200 $300

Linus the Lion stuffed toy
12". POST. 1963. $35 $65 $95 [JR]

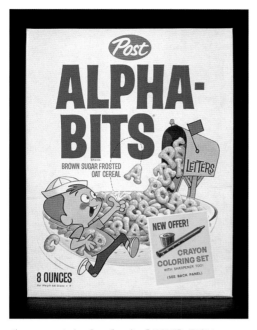

Crayon set (sailor boy)—ALPHA BITS
9.5", POST, 1963. $75 $100 $125

Action football player—RICE KRINKLES
9.25", POST, 1963. $100 $125 $150

Football player (genie boy)—
SUGAR SPARKLED FLAKES
10.5", POST, 1963. $75 $100 $125

Action football player—SUGAR SPARKLED
FLAKES & RICE KRINKLES (bks)
POST, 1963.

Action football players
EA 2.5". POST. 1963.  EA $10 $15 $20 [GT]

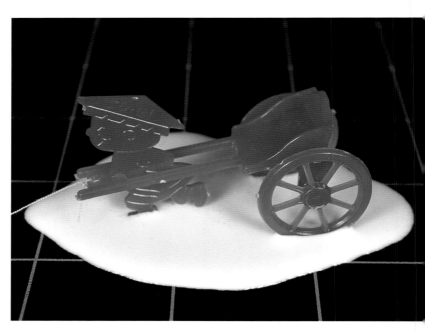

So-Hi ricksaw toy
2.5" LONG. POST. 1963.  $10 $25 $45 [RC]

**3-D jet fighter—GRAPE NUTS FLAKES**
10″. POST. 1963. $25 $45 $65

**A-4 Skyhawk & F-101 Voodoo fighter cut-outs**
EA 5″ X 7″. POST. 1963. EA $3 $5 $7

**3-D jet fighter—GRAPE NUTS FLAKES (bks)**
EA 10″. POST. 1963. EA $25 $45 $65

Introductory FROOT LOOPS (Toucan Sam) "shelf talker" sign
11.5", KELLOGG, 1963. $75 $125 $150

Tony Tiger stuffed toy—FROSTED FLAKES
& "Corny" jingle corntest—CORN FLAKES
11.5"/11.5", KELLOGG, 1963.

Tony Tiger stuffed toy—FROSTED FLAKES (bk)
11.5", KELLOGG, 1963.  $100 $150 $200

Tony Tiger stuffed toy
26". KELLOGG, 1963.  $25 $50 $75

"Corny" jingle corntest—CORN FLAKES (bk)
11.5", KELLOGG. 1963. $25 $50 $75

Musical cornyphone & instructions
9" LONG. KELLOGG. 1963. $5 $20 $35

Scale model 1963 Ford hardtop
8.5" LONG. KELLOGG. 1963. $50 $90 $125 [LB]

TRIPLE SNACK, SUGAR POPS, OKs, & FROSTED FLAKES singles on newspapers
EA 4". KELLOGG, 1963. EA $10 $20 $35

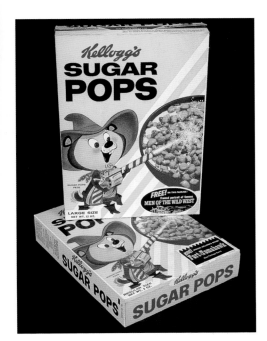

Men of the Wild West & Ft. Tomahawk—SUGAR POPS
KELLOGG. 1963.   EA $75 $100 $125

Men of the Wild West (Gen. Custer)—SUGAR POPS (bk)
11". KELLOGG. 1963.  $75 $100 $125

Ft. Tomahawk playset—SUGAR POPS (bk)
9.75". KELLOGG. 1963.  $75 $100 $125

Bert the Chimney Sweep pop-up (Buffalo Bee)—
WHEAT HONEYS
9.5", NABISCO, 1964. $100 $150 $200

Bert the Chimney Sweep pop-up (Buffalo Bee)—
WHEAT HONEYS (bk)
9.5", NABISCO, 1964. $100 $150 $200

Popeye shirt offer—POPEYE PUFFED WHEAT
14" LONG, PURITY MILLS, 1964. $25 $50 $75

Mary Poppins pop-up (Buffalo Bee)—
RICE HONEYS

9.5", NABISCO, 1964. $100 $150 $200

Mary Poppins pop-up (Buffalo Bee)—
RICE HONEYS (bk)

9.5", NABISCO, 1964. $100 $150 $200

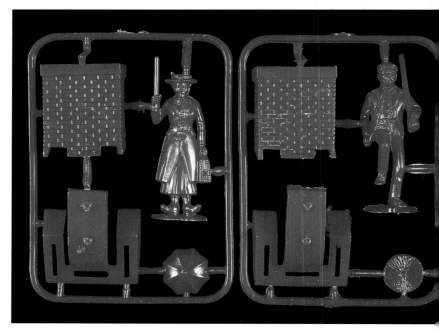

Mary Poppins & Bert the Sweep pop-ups
EA TREE 2.75" X 3.75", NABISCO, 1964. EA $15 $35 $55

Comic rings & Bo'sun whistle—CAP'N CRUNCH
EA 9.5", QUAKER OATS. 1964.

Bo'sun whistle—CAP'N CRUNCH (bk)
9.5", QUAKER OATS, 1964. $100 $150 $200

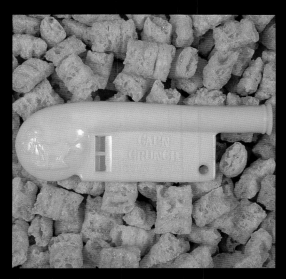

Cap'n Crunch bo'sun whistle
3.25" LONG, QUAKER OATS, 1964. $5 $10 $15

Cap'n Crunch rings—CAP'N CRUNCH (bk)
9.5", QUAKER OATS, 1964. $150 $300 $450

Cap'n Crunch rings
1"-2". QUAKER OATS. 1964. $25-50 $50-100 $75-150 [AC/GT]

Presidential trading cards—JETS
9.5", GENERAL MILLS, 1964.
$25 $50 $75

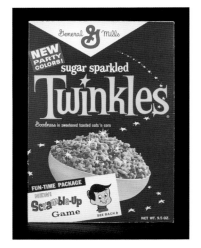

Scramble-up game—TWINKLES
9.5", GENERAL MILLS, 1964.
$50 $75 $100

Trix rabbit breakfast set
STACK 5.5", GENERAL MILLS, 1964.
$75 $100 $125 [RC]

Trix rabbit placemat & breakfast set
PLACEMAT 11.5" X 16.5", GENERAL MILLS, 1964.  $35 $55 $75 [DG/SR]

Hoppity Hooper's lily pad jump—CHEERIOS
& Bullwinkle ring toss—KIX
9.5"/11", GENERAL MILLS, 1964. EA $45 $75 $125

Hoppity Hooper's lily pad jump—CHEERIOS
& Bullwinkle ring toss—KIX (bks)
9.5"/11", GENERAL MILLS, 1964. EA $45 $75 $125

Rocky & Bullwinkle ring toss game & Hoppity Hooper's lily pad jump (cutouts)
GENERAL MILLS, 1964. EA $5 $10 $15

Pick-up sticks (Dandy-style bear)—SUGAR CRISP
9", POST, 1964.  $35 $50 $75

Toy boat (So-Hi)—RICE KRINKLES
7.25", POST, 1964.  $75 $100 $125

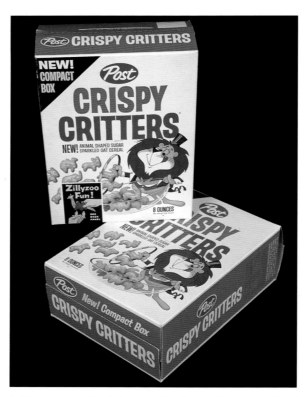

Zillyzoo animals & Linus colorforms (Linus the Lion)—
CRISPY CRITTERS
EA 7.75", POST, 1963-64.  $75-100 $125-150 $150-200

Colorforms (Linus the Lion)—CRISPY CRITTERS (bk)
7.75", POST, 1964. $100 $150 $200

Zillyzoo animals—CRISPY CRITTERS (bk)
7.75", POST, 1963-64. $75 $125 $150

Linus' critter cards
BOX 2.3" X 3.75", POST, 1964. $15 $35 $50

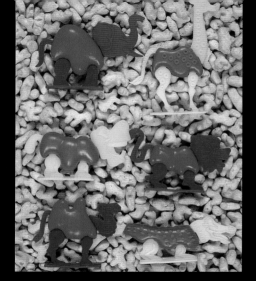

Zillyzoo animals
1.5"-4", POST, 1963-64.  EA $3 $10 $15

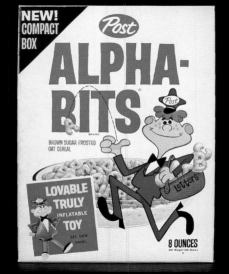

Inflatable/cartoon (Lovable Truly)—
ALPHA BITS
7.75", POST, 1964.  $100 $150 $200

Toy sweepstakes (proto Sugar Bear)—SUGAR CRISP
7.75", POST, 1964.  $75 $100 $125

Adventures from Linus show/inflatable boxes (bks)
EA 9". POST. 1964. $25-75 $50-100 $100-200

Adventures from Linus show—RAISIN BRAN
EA 7.75". POST. 1964. EA $25 $65 $95

Rory Racoon inflatable/comic—TOASTIES
10.5", POST, 1964. $45 $95 $150

Rory Racoon inflatable/comic—TOASTIES (bk)
10.5", POST, 1964. $45 $95 $150

Beverly Hillbillies' "Dern Tootin'" CORN FLAKES counter display
10.5", KELLOGG, 1964. $100 $250 $400

Tony the Tiger mug & bowl—FROSTED FLAKES
11", KELLOGG, 1964. $100 $150 $200

Tony the Tiger mug & bowl—FROSTED FLAKES (bk)
11", KELLOGG, 1964. $100 $150 $200

Tony the Tiger mug & bowl
STACKED 5.5", KELLOGG, 1964. SET $15 $35 $50

Woody Woodpecker doorknocker
5.75", KELLOGG, 1964. $25 $65 $100 [GT]

"Hey, Yogi Bear" record, food bargain, &
"Cornfucius Say" joke book—CORN FLAKES
KELLOGG, 1964.

"Hey, Yogi Bear" record—CORN FLAKES (bk)
9.75". KELLOGG, 1964.  $35 $75 $100

"Hey There, It's Yogi Bear" record
SLEEVE 7.75" X 7.75". KELLOGG, 1964.  $15 $35 $50

Homer & Jethro food bargain—
CORN FLAKES (bks)
9.75"/11", KELLOGG, 1964. EA $15 $45 $65

Homer & Jethro's "Cornfucius Say" joke book—
CORN FLAKES (bk)
9.75", KELLOGG, 1964. $75 $100 $125 [DG/SR]

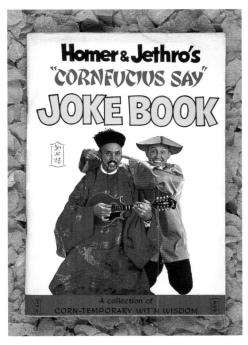

Homer & Jethro's "Cornfucius Say" joke book
7.25" X 5", KELLOGG, 1964. $7 $15 $25 [DG/SR]

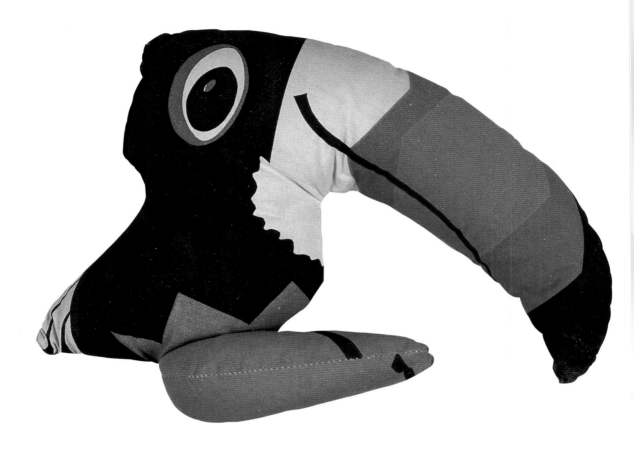

Toucan Sam stuffed toy
8". KELLOGG. 1964. $15 $30 $45

Toucan Sam stuffed toy—FROOT LOOPS
10.5", KELLOGG, 1964.  $100 $250 $400

Toucan Sam stuffed toy—FROOT LOOPS (bk)
10.5", KELLOGG, 1964.  $100 $250 $400

"Sweet Eatin' Bowlers" (two-sided) over-aisle display
7' X 7-10', KELLOGG, 1964.  $750 $1500 $2500

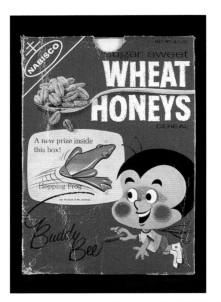

Hopping frog (Buddy Bee)—WHEAT HONEYS

9.5", NABISCO, 1965.  $50 $75 $100

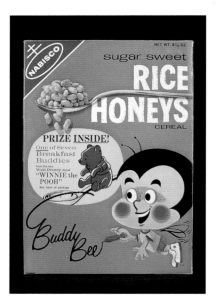

Winnie the Pooh breakfast buddies
(Buddy Bee)—RICE HONEYS

9.5", NABISCO, 1965.  $100 $150 $200

Winnie the Pooh breakfast buddies—
RICE HONEYS (bk)

9.5", NABISCO, 1965.  $100 $150 $200

Winnie the Pooh breakfast buddies
1.75"-2.5". NABISCO. 1965. EA $5 $10 $15

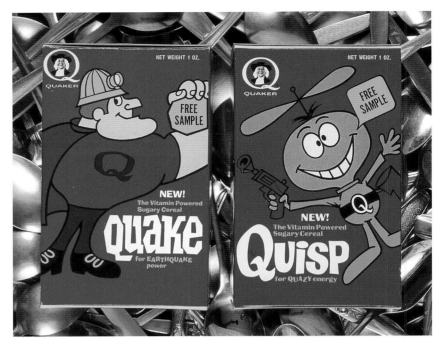

QUAKE & QUISP samples
EA 5.5", QUAKER OATS, 1965.  EA $100 $200 $300

Elizabeth Montgomery DIET FROSTED WHEAT/
RICE PUFFS zine ad
13.5" X 10.5", QUAKER OATS, 1965.  $3 $7 $10

Bewitched hunt game—LIFE (bk)
9.5", QUAKER OATS, 1965.  $15 $35 $55

"Join My Crew" & comic book–CAP'N CRUNCH
9.5"/10.5", QUAKER OATS, 1965.

Cap'n Crunch membership kit
MAILER 9.5" X 12.5", QUAKER OATS, 1965.
$100 $200 $300 [DG/SR]

"Join My Crew"–CAP'N CRUNCH (bk)
9.5", QUAKER OATS, 1965.  $100 $200 $300

Comic books–CAP'N CRUNCH (bk)
10.5", QUAKER OATS, 1965.  $100 $200 $300

Cap'n Crunch comic books
EA 2.5" X 6.5", QUAKER OATS, 1965.  EA $10 $20 $35 [AC/RC]

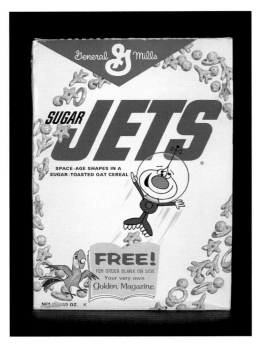

Golden books (Goggol the alien)—SUGAR JETS
9.5", GENERAL MILLS, 1965-66.  $75 $125 $150

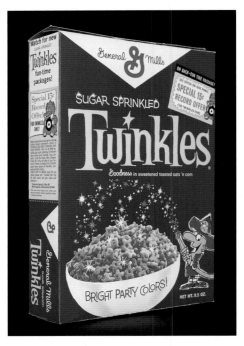

Twinkles record (Twinkles Sprinkler)—TWINKLES
9.5", GENERAL MILLS, 1965.  $100 $150 $200

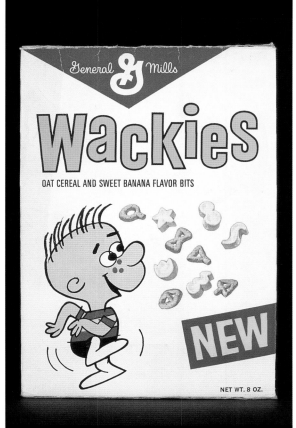

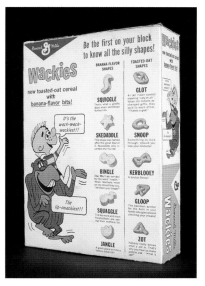

Introductory—WACKIES (bk)
9.5", GENERAL MILLS, 1965.  $100 $175 $250

Introductory (Wackies boy)—WACKIES
9.5". GENERAL MILLS, 1965.  $100 $175 $250

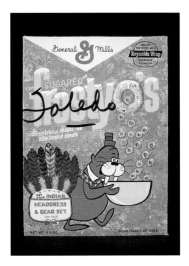

Indian headdress (Clumley)—FROSTYO'S
9.5", GENERAL MILLS, 1965.  $100 $200 $300

Tennessee Tuxedo national park album
& Bullwinkle trading cards–KIX
EA 11", GENERAL MILLS, 1965.

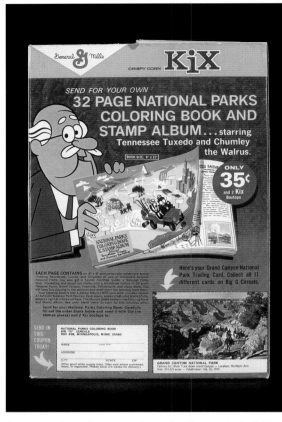

Tennessee Tuxedo national park album–KIX (bk)
11", GENERAL MILLS, 1965.  $75 $125 $150

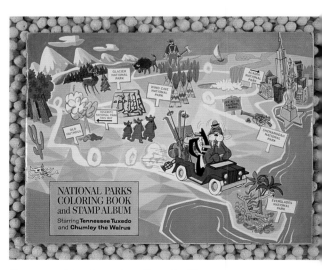

Tennessee Tuxedo national park album
8.25" X 11", GENERAL MILLS, 1965.  $15 $35 $60

Rocky & Bullwinkle trading cards—KIX (bk)
11", GENERAL MILLS, 1965. $75 $125 $150

Rocky & Bullwinkle trading cards
EA 1.25" X 2", GENERAL MILLS, 1965. EA $1 $2 $3

TV star pix, TV quiz, & Sherman/Peabody op-tricks—CHEERIOS
11"/9.5"/9.5"/9.5", GENERAL MILLS, 1965.  $25-50 $75-100 $125-150

TV star action picture #1—CHEERIOS (bk)
11", GENERAL MILLS, 1965.  $25 $75 $125

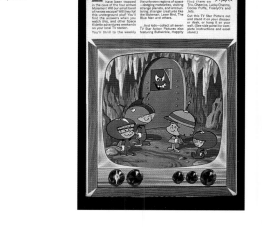

TV star pix, TV quiz, & Sherman/Peabody op-tricks—CHEERIOS (bks)
9.5"/9.5"/9.5", GENERAL MILLS, 1965.  $25-50 $75-100 $125-150

Walky squawky talkies—TRIX

9.5", GENERAL MILLS, 1965.  $100 $175 $250

Walky squawky talkies—TRIX (bk)

9.5", GENERAL MILLS, 1965.  $100 $175 $250

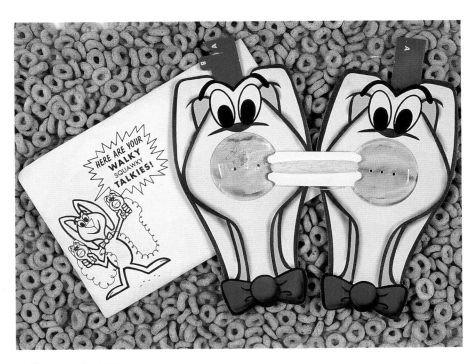

Walky squawky talkies

MAILER 4.5" X 7", GENERAL MILLS, 1965.  $10 $25 $45 [RC]

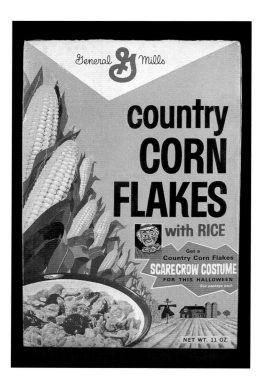

Mr. Scarecrow costume—COUNTRY CORN FLAKES
11.25", GENERAL MILLS, 1965. $75 $125 $150 [RC]

Mr. Scarecrow costume—COUNTRY CORN FLAKES (bk)
11.25", GENERAL MILLS, 1965. $75 $125 $150 [RC]

Mr. Scarecrow costume
GENERAL MILLS. 1965. $35 $60 $85

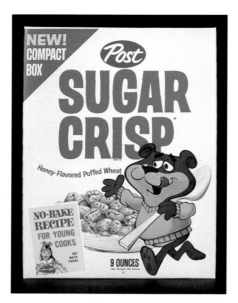

No-bake recipe (Sugar Bear)—SUGAR CRISP
7.75". POST. 1965. $50 $75 $100

Spring-n-string action toy (So-Hi)—KRINKLES
7.25". POST. 1965. $100 $175 $250

Spring-n-string action toy—KRINKLES (bk)
7.25". POST. 1965. $100 $175 $250

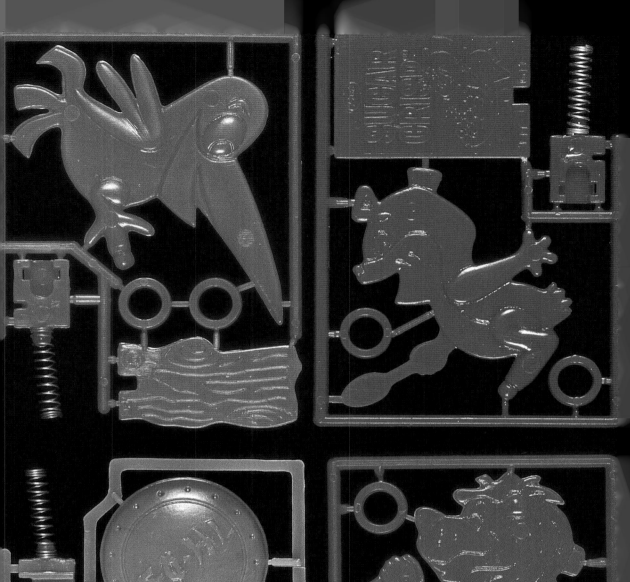

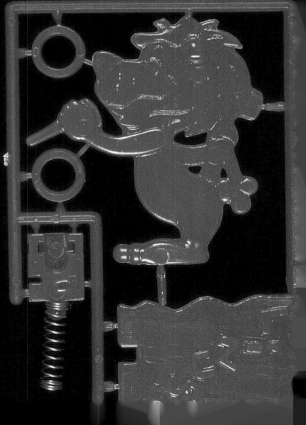

Pink elephant toy—CRISPY CRITTERS
8", POST, 1965. $100 $150 $200

Pink elephant toy—CRISPY CRITTERS (bk)
8", POST, 1965. $100 $150 $200

Linus the Lionhearted record album
12.5" X 12.5". POST. 1965. $15 $30 $45 [GT]

Linus the Lion record—CRISPY CRITTERS (bk)
9.5". POST. 1965. $100 $175 $250

Laurence the Dog (Lovable Truly's nemesis) costume
STORE ITEM. POST. 1965. $50 $75 $100 [RC]

Jimmy Durante food bargain—CORN FLAKES (bks)
EA 9.75", KELLOGG, 1965. EA $25 $50 $75

"Doin' the Flake" record & Durante food bargain—
CORN FLAKES
11"/9.75", KELLOGG, 1965.

Gary Lewis "Doin' the Flake" record—
CORN FLAKES (bk)
11", KELLOGG, 1965. $75 $125 $175

Gary Lewis "Doin' the Flake" records & coupon
SLEEVE 7" X 7", KELLOGG, 1965. EA $15 $30 $45 [AC/GT]

Jimmy Durante "Yes we now have bananas" zine ad
13.5" X 10.5", KELLOGG, 1965. $5 $7 $10

Introductory (Pronto Banana Man)—CORN FLAKES
WITH INSTANT BANANAS
9", KELLOGG, 1965. $75 $150 $225

Introductory (Apple Jack)—APPLE JACKS
9", KELLOGG, 1965. $100 $175 $250

Treats (Snap) & Woody Woodpecker mug & bowl
(Pop)–RICE KRISPIES
9.75"/9", KELLOGG, 1965. $15-50 $25-100 $50-150

Woody Woodpecker mug & bowl–
RICE KRISPIES (bk)
9", KELLOGG, 1965. $50 $100 $150

Woody Woodpecker mug & bowl
3.5"/6" LONG, KELLOGG, 1965. SET $15 $25 $35

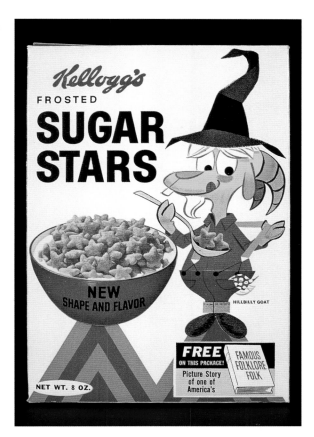

Famous folklore folks (Hillbilly Goat)—
SUGAR STARS

9". KELLOGG. 1965. $75 $125 $150

Famous folklore folks boxes (bks)

EA 9". KELLOGG. 1965. $15-100 $35-200 $75-300

Masters of the sea (blue giraffe)—TRIPLE SNACK
8", KELLOGG, 1965. $100 $200 $300

Masters of the sea boxes (bks)
EA 8-9", KELLOGG, 1965. $15-100 $35-200 $75-300

Contest/Yogi bank—FROOT LOOPS & RAISIN BRAN
10.5"/9", KELLOGG, 1965. $15-75 $45-150 $65-250

Yogi Bear bank (3rd prize)
9.5", KELLOGG, 1965. $10 $25 $35

Mickey Mouse & Donald Duck--PUPPETS
EA 10". NABISCO, 1966. EA $10 $25 $50

Kanga/Roo & Winnie the Pooh--PUPPETS
EA 10". NABISCO, 1966. EA $35 $75 $100

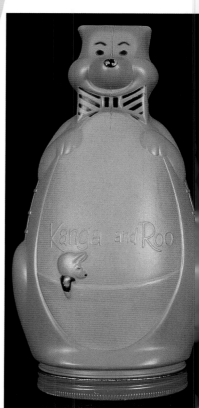

Checkerboard Squarecrow doll—CORN CHEX
11.25". RALSTON. 1966-67. $35 $65 $95

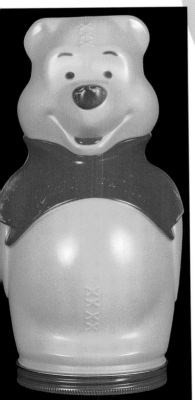

Checkerboard Squarecrow doll—CORN CHEX (bk)
11.25". RALSTON. 1966-67. $35 $65 $95

Cereal bowls, treasure chest, & official compass—CAP'N CRUNCH
QUAKER OATS, 1966.

Cereal bowl & official compass—CAP'N CRUNCH (bks)
EA 10.25", QUAKER OATS, 1966  $75-125 $125-175 $250-300.

Checkerboard Squarecrow doll
21", RALSTON, 1966-67.  $15 $45 $75

Official Cap'n Crunch compass & Cap'n cereal bowls
COMPASS 8.5" LONG. QUAKER OATS, 1966. $15 $45 $75
BOWLS EA 4.75" X 4.75". QUAKER OATS, 1966. EA $10 $20 $30 [DG/SR/GT]

Treasure chest—CAP'N CRUNCH (bk)
9.5". QUAKER OATS, 1966. $100 $200 $300

Cap'n Crunch treasure chest
4" X 6" X 5", QUAKER OATS, 1966. $15 $45 $75

Cap'n Crunch & crew hand puppets
EA 9", QUAKER OATS, 1966. EA $10 $20 $35 [RC]

FREE
QUISP
RING
INSIDE

QUAKER

The Vitamin Powered
Sugary Cereal

QUiSP

for QUAZY energy

NET WEIGHT 8 OZ.

NEW!
The Vitamin Powered
Sugary Cereal

QUiSP

for QUAZY energy

FREE
COMIC
BOOK
INSIDE

NET WEIGHT 8 OZ.

Vitamin Powered
Sugar Sweet

QUiSP

for QUAZY energy

QUISP—the only cereal
better than QUAKE

QUISP is the
only cereal
better than
QUAKE

QUiSP

for QUAZY energy

Comic books—QUAKE
10.5", QUAKER OATS, 1966. $200 $450 $750

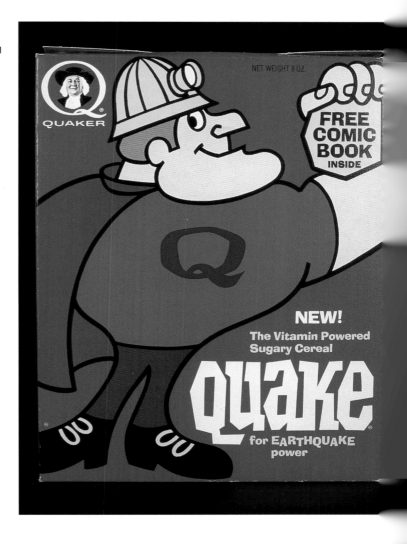

Comic books—QUISP & QUAKE (bks)
10.5", QUAKER OATS, 1966. EA $200 $450 $750

Quisp rings & comic book—QUISP
EA 10.5", QUAKER OATS, 1966. EA $200 $450 $750

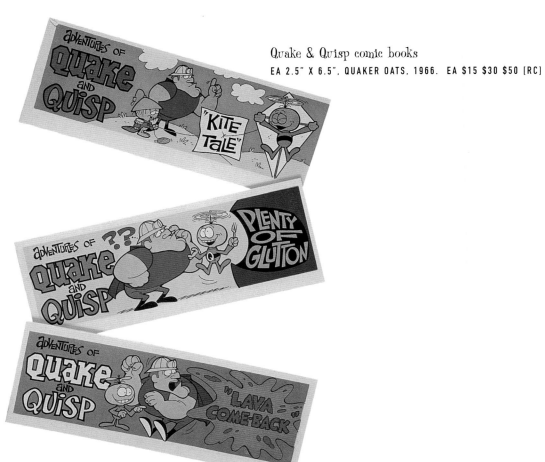

Quake & Quisp comic books
EA 2.5" X 6.5", QUAKER OATS, 1966. EA $15 $30 $50 [RC]

Quisp rings—QUISP (bk)
10.5", QUAKER OATS, 1966. $200 $450 $750

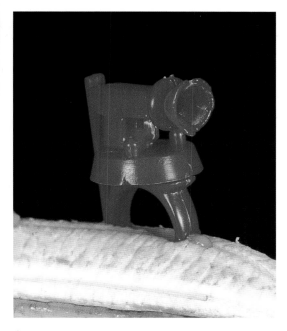

Quisp space gun ring
ABOUT 1.5", QUAKER OATS. 1966.  $100 $200 $300 [AS]

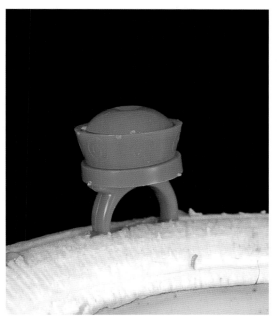

Quisp space disk whistle ring
ABOUT 1", QUAKER OATS. 1966.  $100 $200 $300 [AS]

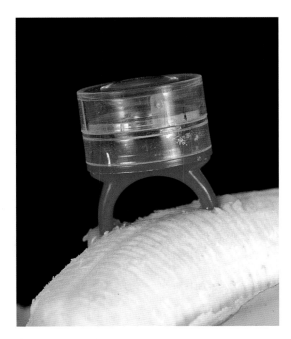

Quisp meteorite ring
ABOUT 1", QUAKER OATS. 1966.  $100 $200 $300 [AS]

Quisp friendship ring
1.75", QUAKER OATS. 1966.  $300 $600 $900 [AS]

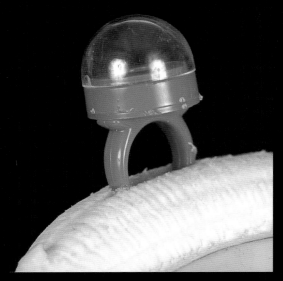

Quake leaping lava ring
ABOUT 1.25", QUAKER OATS, 1966.  $100 $250 $350 [AS]

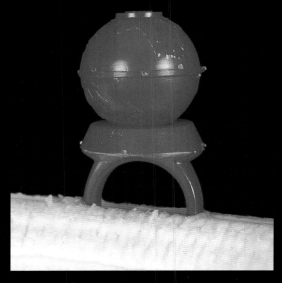

Quake world globe ring
ABOUT 1.5", QUAKER OATS, 1966.  $200 $400 $600 [AS]

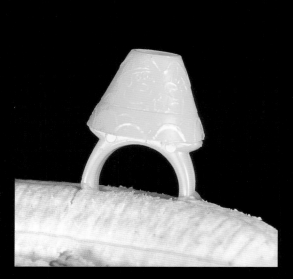

Quake volcano whistle ring
ABOUT 1", QUAKER OATS, 1966.  $100 $200 $300 [AS]

Quake friendship ring
1.75", QUAKER OATS, 1966.  $150 $300 $450 [AS]

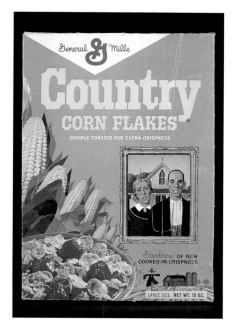

(American Gothic couple)—COUNTRY CORN FLAKES
11". GENERAL MILLS. 1966. $10 $20 $30

Bob Richards "raw wheat," commercial—
WHEATIES
12.25". GENERAL MILLS. 1966. $10 $25 $45

Bob Richards "raw wheat," commercial—WHEATIES (bk)
12.25". GENERAL MILLS. 1966. $10 $25 $45

Kix character recipe & trading cards–KIX
EA 11", GENERAL MILLS, 1966.  EA $25 $50 $75

Kix character trading cards (cutouts)
EA 2.5" X 3", GENERAL MILLS, 1966.  EA $2 $5 $7

Bullwinkle comic, follow the colors portrait,
& coloring tile set—CHEERIOS
10.5"/10.5"/9.5". GENERAL MILLS. 1966.

Bullwinkle comic, follow the colors portrait, & coloring tile set—CHEERIOS (bks)
GENERAL MILLS. 1966.  $35-65 $75-100 $125-150

Jim Nabors–TOASTIES, Mustang model–TOASTIES,
& Andy Griffith–GRAPE NUTS FLAKES
POST, 1966.

Andy Griffith's recipe–GRAPE NUTS FLAKES
& Jim Nabors' recipe–TOASTIES (bks)
8"/10.5", POST, 1966.  EA $75 $150 $200

Ford Mustang models–TOASTIES (bk)
8.5", POST, 1966.  $75 $100 $125

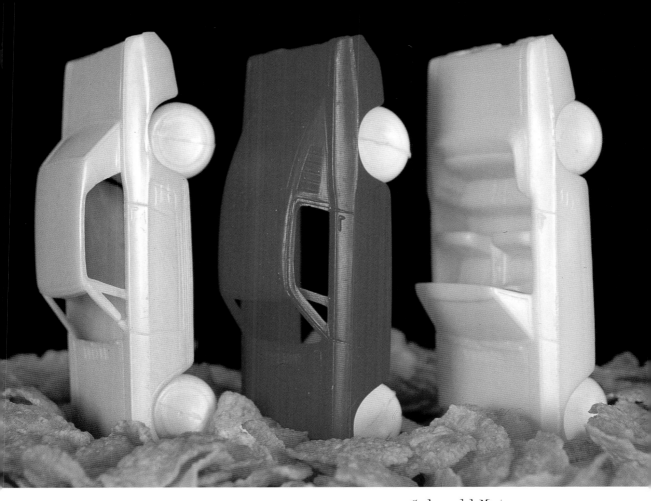

Scale-model Mustangs
EA 3" LONG, POST, 1966.  EA $5 $10 $15

Paddle wheel boats & spy-master
command belt (So-Hi)—KRINKLES
EA 8", POST, 1966.  EA $100 $200 $300

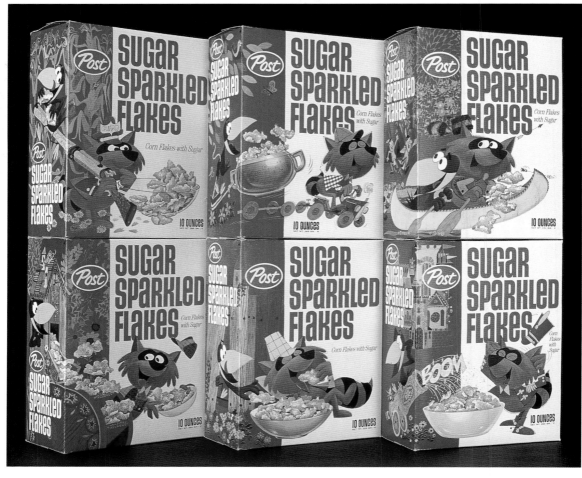

Fun 'n games (Rory Raccoon)—SUGAR SPARKLED FLAKES sextet.
EA 8". POST. 1966.  EA $75 $125 $175

Honeycomb Kid ring, spy-master command belt,
& picture puzzle—HONEYCOMB
EA 9". POST. 1966.

Honeycomb Kid 24 carat gold ring (scratched dome)
1", POST, 1966.  $25 $75 $125

Spy-master command belt—HONEYCOMB (bk)
9", POST, 1966.  $75 $100 $125

Honeycomb Kid picture puzzle—HONEYCOMB (bks)
EA 9", POST, 1966.  EA $50 $75 $100

Honeycomb Kid ring—HONEYCOMB (bk)
9", POST, 1966.  $75 $100 $125

Spy-master command belt
31" LONG, POST, 1966.   $25 $55 $75 [AS]

Lovable Truly inflatable, mystery diver,
& '67 Mercury Cougar—ALPHA BITS
EA 9", POST, 1966.

Mystery diver—ALPHA BITS (bk)
9" LONG, POST, 1966.   $65 $115 $165

1967 Mercury Cougar—ALPHA BITS (bk)
9". POST. 1966. $75 $125 $175

1967 Mercury Cougar scale models
EA 3" LONG. POST. 1966-67. EA $2 $5 $10

Mystery diver
2.5". POST. 1966. $7 $15 $25

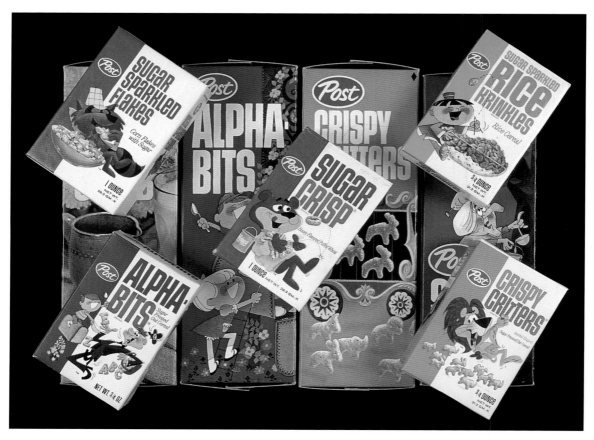

SPARKLED FLAKES, ALPHA BITS, SUGAR CRISP, CRISPY CRITTERS, & KRINKLES singles
EA 4". POST. 1966.  $5-15 $15-30 $25-45

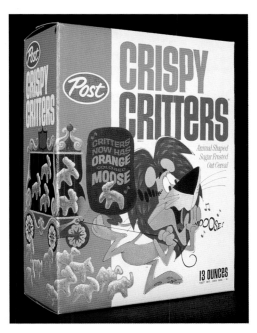

Linus inflatable or puppet theater (Now Orange Moose)—
CRISPY CRITTERS

9", POST, 1966.  EA $100 $175 $250

Puppet theater—CRISPY CRITTERS (bk)

9", POST, 1966.  $100 $175 $250

Post puppet theater
10" X 18" X 15". POST. 1966. $100 $150 $200 [DG/SR]

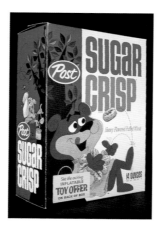

Sugar Bear inflatable—SUGAR CRISP
9". POST. 1966. $100 $175 $250

Character inflatables—SUGAR CRISP, CRISPY CRITTERS, & ALPHA BITS (bks)
EA 9". POST. 1966. $75-100 $150-200 $250-300

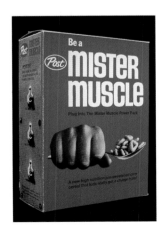

Introductory MISTER MUSCLE
9". POST. 1966. $75 $125 $175

Introductory MISTER MUSCLE (bk)
9". POST. 1966. $75 $125 $175

CORN FLAKES & PEACHES, BLUEBERRIES, & STRAWBERRIES
EA 10"/7". POST. 1966. $10-15 $20-25 $30-40

Smackin' Brothers jig-jag puzzle—SUGAR SMACKS
10". KELLOGG. 1966. $75 $125 $175

Smackin' Brothers jig-jag puzzle—
SUGAR SMACKS (bk)
10". KELLOGG. 1966. $75 $125 $175

Smackin' Brothers jig-jag puzzle cutout
5.75" X 5.5". KELLOGG. 1966. $3 $5 $7

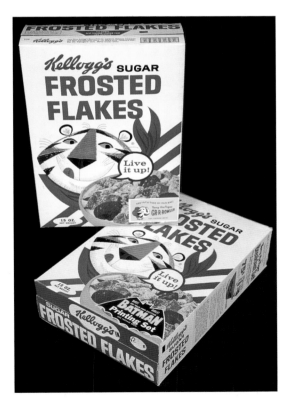

Tony the Tiger gr-r-rowler & Batman printing set—
FROSTED FLAKES
EA 10". KELLOGG. 1966. $50-125 $95-250 $125-400

Tony the Tiger gr-r-rowler—FROSTED FLAKES (bk)
10". KELLOGG. 1966. $50 $95 $125

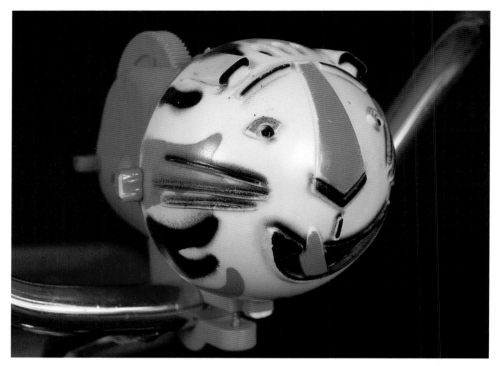

Tony the Tiger gr-r-rowler
4.5" LONG. KELLOGG. 1966. $50 $95 $125

Woody Woodpecker puzzles & stuffed toy—
RICE KRISPIES
9"/10"/11". KELLOGG. 1966. $10-35 $25-75 $35-125

Woody Woodpecker puzzles & stuffed toy—
RICE KRISPIES (bks)
9"/10"/11". KELLOGG. 1966. $10-35 $25-75 $35-125

Hillbilly Goat stuffed toy—STARS
9", KELLOGG, 1966. $100 $150 $200

Hillbilly Goat stuffed toy—STARS (bk)
9", KELLOGG, 1966. $100 $150 $200

Woody Woodpecker & Hillbilly Goat stuffed toys
13"/14", KELLOGG, 1966. EA $15 $30 $45

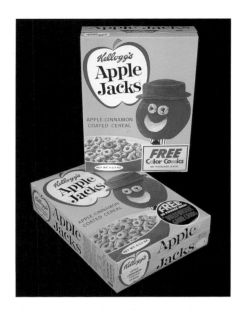

Color comics & bully-buster card game—
APPLE JACKS
EA 9", KELLOGG, 1966.  EA $75 $150 $225

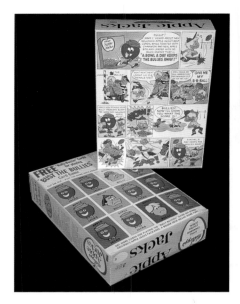

Color comics & bully-buster card game—
APPLE JACKS (bks)
EA 9", KELLOGG, 1966.  EA $75 $150 $225

Batman periscope—FROOT LOOPS &
Batman printing set—RAISIN BRAN
10"/8", KELLOGG, 1966.

Batman periscope—FROOT LOOPS (bk)
10", KELLOGG, 1966.  $125 $250 $400

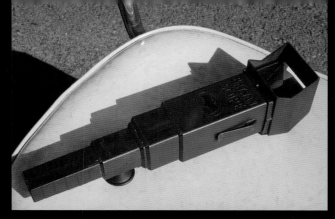

Batman periscope
11"-21" LONG. KELLOGG. 1966. $35 $50 $75 [BK]

Batman printing set—RAISIN BRAN (bk)
8". KELLOGG. 1966. $100 $200 $300

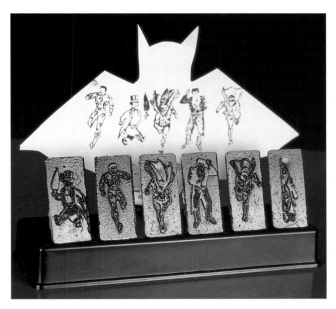

Batman printing set
CASE 4.5 LONG". KELLOGG. 1966. $15 $30 $45

Bambi puppet show—RICE HONEYS
9.5", NABISCO, 1967. $100 $175 $250 [RC]

Snow White walking Dwarfs—RICE HONEYS
9.5", NABISCO, 1967. $75 $125 $175 [RC]

Walking Dwarfs & Bambi puppet show—HONEYS (bks)
EA 9.5", NABISCO, 1967. $75-100 $125-175 $175-250 [RC]

Dwarf walkers & tunnel cutout
EA 2.25" LONG, NABISCO, 1967. EA $10 $20 $30 [RC]

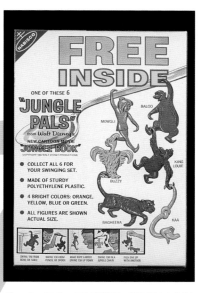

Jungle Pals—WHEAT HONEYS
**9.5", NABISCO, 1967.  $75 $125 $175**

Jungle Pals—WHEAT HONEYS (bk)
**9.5", NABISCO, 1967.  $75 $125 $175**

Jungle Book pals
**EA 1.5"-3" LONG, NABISCO, 1967.  EA $5 $10 $15**

Guppy model—CAP'N CRUNCH

10.5", QUAKER OATS, 1967. $100 $250 $400

Guppy model—CAP'N CRUNCH (bk)

10.5", QUAKER OATS, 1967. $100 $250 $400

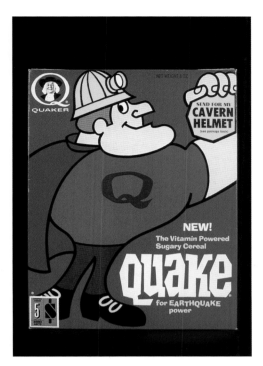

Cavern helmet—QUAKE (bk)
10.5", QUAKER OATS, 1967.  $150 $350 $500

Cavern helmet—QUAKE
10.5", QUAKER OATS, 1967.  $150 $350 $500

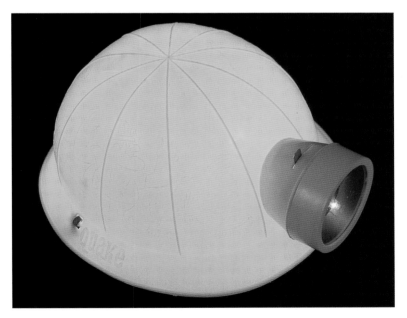

Quake cavern helmet
10" LONG, QUAKER OATS, 1967.  $100 $225 $350 [RC]

Guppy model
10" LONG, QUAKER OATS, 1967.  $100 $200 $300

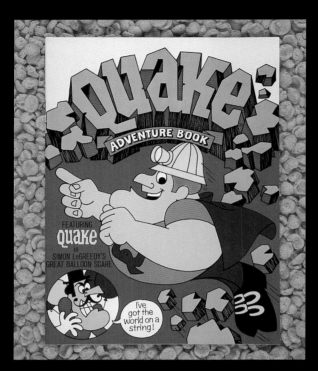

Quake adventure book

8.25" X 11", QUAKER OATS, 1968. $35 $65 $100 [RC]

Quake adventure book (bk cover)

8.25" X 11", QUAKER OATS, 1968. $35 $65 $100 [RC]

Quisp propellor beanie
9.5" LONG, QUAKER OATS, 1967. $100 $300 $500

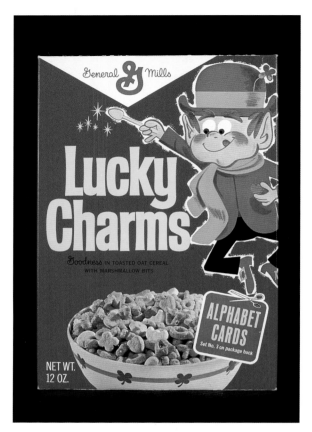

Alphabet cards (Lucky Leprechaun)—LUCKY CHARMS
11", GENERAL MILLS, 1967. $75 $125 $150

Bullwinkle shuffle-O & comics—CHEERIOS
EA 9.5", GENERAL MILLS, 1967. EA $75 $125 $150

Bullwinkle shuffle-O & comics—CHEERIOS (bks)
EA 9.5" TALL, GENERAL MILLS, 1967. EA $75 $125 $150

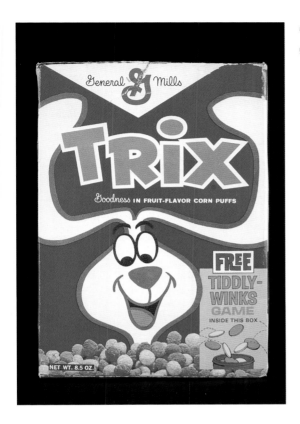

Tiddly-winks game—TRIX
9.5", GENERAL MILLS, 1967. $100 $150 $200

Sample & trial size—CORN CRACKOS
EA 6.5", POST, 1967. EA $75 $100 $125

Linus the Lion fun book—CRISPY CRITTERS
EA 9", POST, 1967.  EA $100 $200 $300

Linus the Lion fun book—CRISPY CRITTERS (bk)
9". POST. 1967. $100 $200 $300

Honeycomb Kid rescue kit—HONEYCOMB
EA 9". POST. 1967. $75 $125 $175

Linus the Lion fun book
5" X 7". POST. 1967. $10 $25 $45

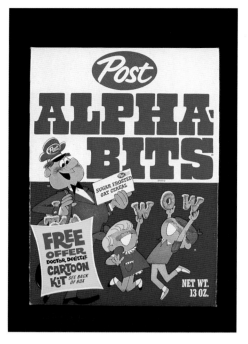

Dr. Dolittle colorforms (Lovable Truly)—
ALPHA BITS
9.5", POST, 1967. $100 $175 $225

Dr. Dolittle colorforms—ALPHA BITS (bk)
9.5", POST, 1967. $100 $175 $225

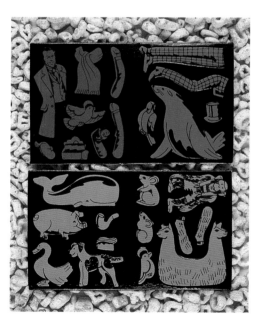

Dr. Dolittle colorforms
EA SHEET 3.5" X 3.5", POST, 1967. SET $15 $35 $50 [RC]

Dr. Dolittle cards & magic paint book—
HONEYCOMB
EA 9.5", POST, 1967. EA $100 $150 $200

Dr. Dolittle cards

**BOX 2.35" X 3.75". POST. 1967. $10 $30 $50**

Dr. Dolittle cards—HONEYCOMB (bk)

**9.5". POST. 1967. $100 $150 $200**

Dr. Dolittle magic paint book—
HONEYCOMB (bk)

**9.5". POST. 1967. $100 $150 $200**

Dr. Dolittle cash carnival—TOASTIES &
GRAPE NUTS FLAKES
11"/8", POST, 1967.  EA $25 $75 $125

Dr. Dolittle cash carnival—TOASTIES, GRAPE NUTS FLAKES, & GRAPE NUTS (bks)
11"/8"/7.75", POST, 1967.  EA $25 $75 $125

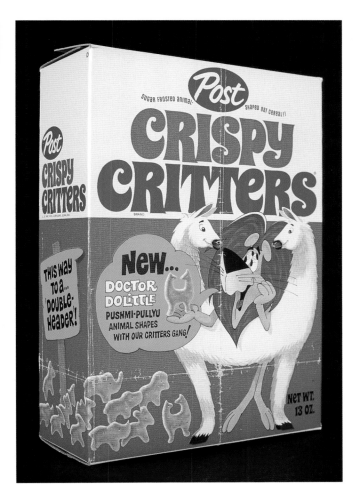

Dr. Dolittle medical kit (Pushmi-Pullyu)—
CRISPY CRITTERS
9.75", POST, 1967. $100 $225 $350

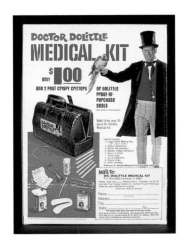

Dr. Dolittle medical kit (Pushmi-Pullyu)—CRISPY CRITTERS (bk)
9.75", POST, 1967. $100 $225 $350

Monkees flicker ring & Davy Jones autographed picture—
PUFFA PUFFA RICE
EA 9", KELLOGG, 1967.

Davy Jones "autographed" picture—
PUFFA PUFFA RICE (bk)
9", KELLOGG, 1967. $100 $225 $350

Monkees flicker ring—
PUFFA PUFFA RICE (bk)
9", KELLOGG, 1967. $100 $250 $400

Monkees flicker rings
EA .75", KELLOGG, 1967. EA $15 $30 $45 [RC]

Monkees picture coins—RAISIN BRAN &
Batman ring—RICE KRISPIES
CAN KELLOGG, 1967.

Monkees picture coins—RAISIN BRAN (bk)
9", CAN KELLOGG, 1967. $100 $200 $300

Monkees picture coins
1.3" ACROSS, KELLOGG, 1967. EA $15 $30 $45

Batman ring
2.5" WIDE, KELLOGG, 1967.  $5 $10 $15

Batman ring—RICE KRISPIES (bk)
10.25", CAN KELLOGG, 1967.  $100 $225 $350

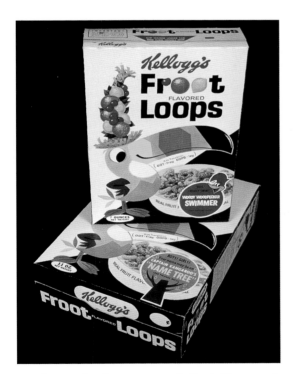

Woody Woodpecker swimmer & Capt. Kangaroo's
name tree—FROOT LOOPS
KELLOGG, 1967.

Capt. Kangaroo's name tree—FROOT LOOPS (bk)
& rescue copter—FROSTED FLAKES
10"/10", KELLOGG, 1967.  LOOPS $100 $225 $350

Rescue copter—FROSTED FLAKES (bk)
10"/10". KELLOGG. 1967. $45 $75 $95

Woody Woodpecker swimmer—FROOT LOOPS (bk)
9". KELLOGG. 1967. $100 $250 $400

Tony the Tiger swimmer
7.5". KELLOGG. 1967.  $75 $100 $125

Smackin' Bros. comics—SUGAR SMACKS
9"/10", KELLOGG, 1967.  EA $75 $125 $175

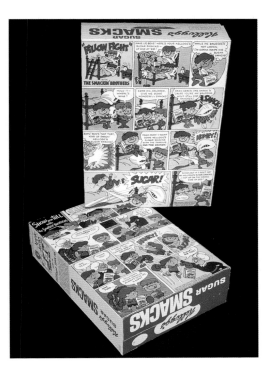

Smackin' Bros. comics—SUGAR SMACKS (bk)
9"/10", KELLOGG, 1967.  EA $75 $125 $175

Recipe (new Snag)—COCOA KRISPIES
& recipe (Yogi)—OKs
9"/10". KELLOGG. 1967. EA $100 $250 $350

Apple Jacks mug & bowl—APPLE JACKS
9". KELLOGG. 1967. $100 $250 $400

Apple Jacks mug & bowl—APPLE JACKS (bk)
9". KELLOGG. 1967. $100 $250 $400

Apple Jacks mug & bowl
3.75"/5.75" ACROSS, KELLOGG, 1967.  SET $50 $100 $150

Wild-wild animal—WHEAT HONEYS
9.5", NABISCO, 1968-69.  $45 $85 $125

Sea monsters—RICE HONEYS
9.5", NABISCO, 1968.  $50 $95 $135

Sea monsters—RICE HONEYS (bk)
9.5", NABISCO, 1968.  $50 $95 $135

Sea monsters
2"-6" LONG, NABISCO, 1968.  EA $2 $5 $7

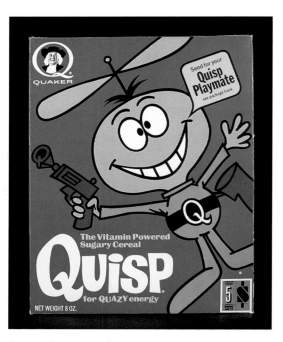

Quisp playmate—QUISP
10.5", QUAKER OATS, 1968. $200 $450 $750

Quisp playmate—QUISP (bk)
10.5", QUAKER OATS, 1968. $200 $450 $750

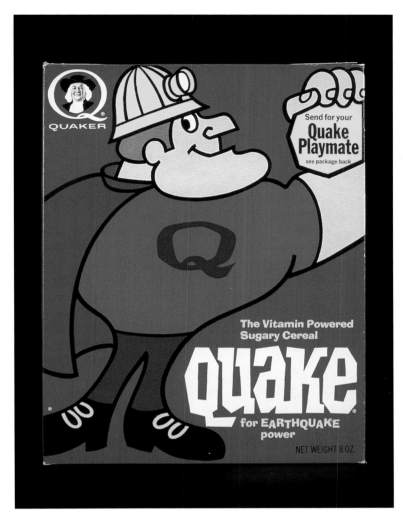

Quake playmate–QUAKE
10.5". QUAKER OATS. 1968.  $200 $450 $750

Quake playmate–QUAKE (bk)
10.5". QUAKER OATS. 1968.  $200 $450 $750

Quisp & Quake playmates
EA 11". QUAKER OATS. 1968. EA $50 $75 $100

Quake mini-nodder
3", CAN QUAKER OATS. 1968. $25 $90 $150 [AS]

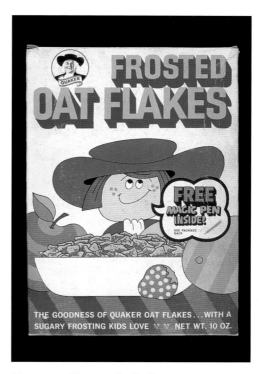

Magic pen (Quincy Quaker)—
FROSTED OAT FLAKES
10", QUAKER OATS. 1968. $75 $100 $125

3-D viewer—WINNIE THE POOH HUNNY MUNCH
9.5", CAN QUAKER OATS. 1968. $100 $175 $250

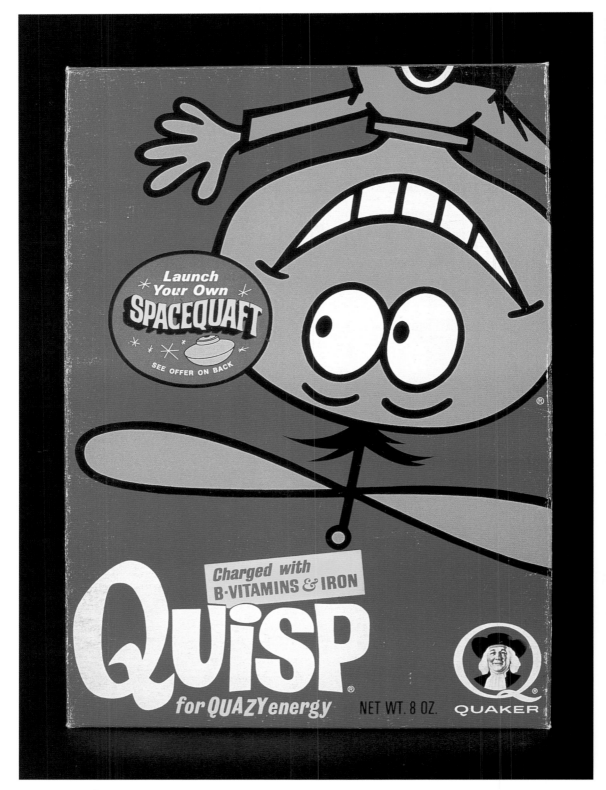

SpaceQuaft—QUISP

10", QUAKER OATS, 1968. $200 $450 $750

SpaceQuaft—QUISP (bk)
10", QUAKER OATS, 1968. $200 $450 $750

Flying Leprechaun glider—LUCKY CHARMS
9.5", GENERAL MILLS, 1968.  $75 $125 $150

Flying Leprechaun glider—LUCKY CHARMS (bk)
9.5", GENERAL MILLS, 1968.  $75 $125 $150

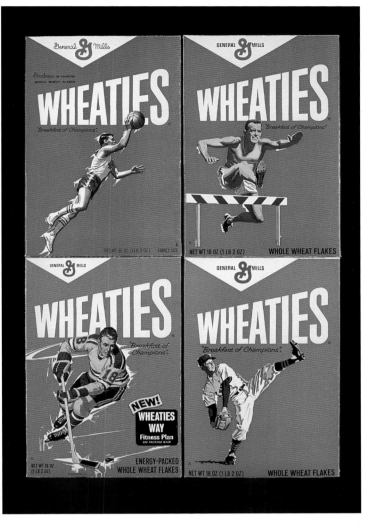

Seasonal sport/player tribute—WHEATIES
EA 12", GENERAL MILLS, 1968. $10-25 $20-50 $45-90

Seasonal sport/player tribute—WHEATIES (bks)
EA 12", GENERAL MILLS, 1968. $10-25 $20-50 $45-90

Miniature license plates—CRISPY CRITTERS
& KRINKLES

9.5"/8", POST, 1968.  EA $100 $200 $300

Adventures of Sugar Bear—SUPER SUGAR
CRISP (bks)

EA 10", POST, 1968.  EA $75 $100 $125

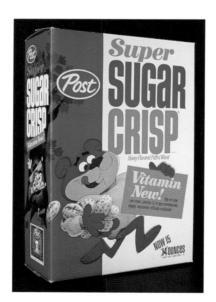

Adventures of Sugar Bear—SUPER SUGAR CRISP

10", POST, 1968.  $75 $125 $150

Magic monocle pix—CORN CRACKOS
8.5", POST, 1968.  $75 $125 $150

Magic monocle pix—CORN CRACKOS (bks)
EA 8.5", POST, 1968.  EA $75 $125 $150

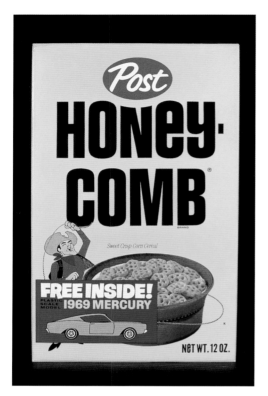

1968 Mercury model (Honeycomb Kid)—HONEYCOMB
11", POST, 1968. $75 $125 $150

1968 Mercury model—HONEYCOMB (bk)
11", POST, 1968. $75 $125 $150

1968 Lincoln-Mercury scale models
EA 3.2" LONG, POST, 1968. EA $10 $15 $20 [LB]

Jim Nabors' country store—PUFFED CORN FLAKES,
KRINKLES, & BRAN FLAKES
9"/9"/10.25". POST, 1968. $10-25 $20-35 $30-65

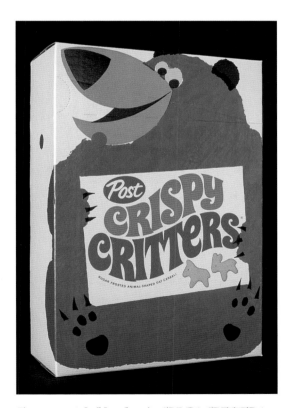

Experimental (blue bear)—CRISPY CRITTERS
9.5". POST, 1968. $100 $200 $300

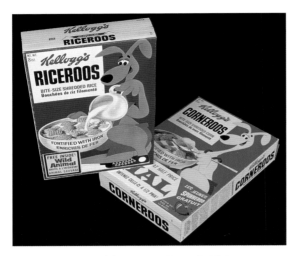

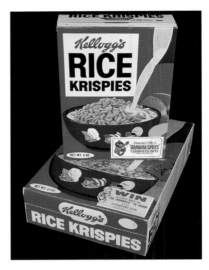

Introductory RICEROOS & CORNEROOS
EA 10.25". CAN KELLOGG. 1968.  EA $35 $75 $100

Banana Splits stampets & Monkees contest—
RICE KRISPIES
9"/11". KELLOGG. 1968.

(Smackin' Bros.)—SMACKS & (Ogg the caveman)—COCOA KRISPIES singles
EA 4". KELLOGG. 1967-68.  EA $10 $25 $50

Monkees contest—RICE KRISPIES (bk)
11", KELLOGG, 1968. $75 $125 $175

Banana Splits stampets—RICE KRISPIES (bk)
9", KELLOGG, 1968. $100 $200 $300

Banana Splits stampets
CASE 4.5" LONG, KELLOGG, 1968. $25 $50 $75 [RC]

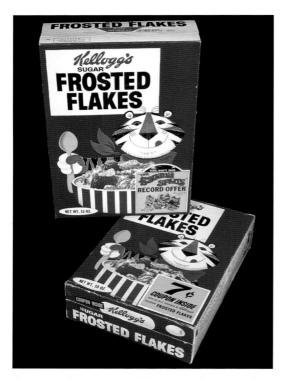

Banana Splits records & Tony the Tiger bank—
FROSTED FLAKES
10"/9" LONG, KELLOGG, 1968.

Tony the Tiger bank—FROSTED FLAKES (bk)
9" LONG, KELLOGG, 1968. $75 $150 $225

Tony the Tiger cookie jar
7.5", KELLOGG, 1968. $35 $65 $95 [ES]

Tony the Tiger toy bank
8.75", KELLOGG, 1968.  $25 $50 $75

Banana Splits records—FROSTED FLAKES (bk)
10", KELLOGG, 1968.  $100 $225 $350

Banana Splits records
SLEEVE 7" X 7", KELLOGG, 1968.  EA $25 $45 $65

Yellow Submarine rub-ons—WHEAT HONEYS

9.5". NABISCO. 1969.  $250 $500 $750

Yellow Submarine rub-ons—WHEAT & RICE HONEYS (bks)
EA 9.5" TALL, NABISCO, 1969.  EA $250 $500 $750

Yellow Submarine rub-ons—
RICE HONEYS
9.5", NABISCO, 1969.  $250 $500 $750

Yellow Submarine rub-ons
EA SHEET 3.5" X 2.5", NABISCO, 1969.  EA $25 $45 $75

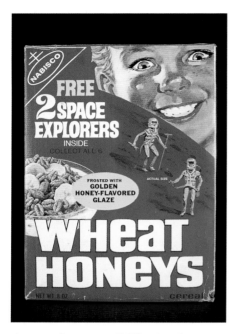

Space explorers—WHEAT HONEYS
9.5". NABISCO. 1969. $75 $100 $150

Space explorers—WHEAT HONEYS (bk)
9.5". NABISCO. 1969. $75 $100 $150

Space explorers
EA 2". NABISCO. 1969. EA $1 $3 $5

Wiggle figures—CRUNCH BERRIES
10", QUAKER OATS, 1969. $200 $300 $400

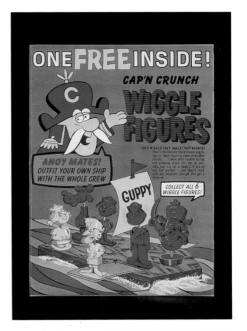

Wiggle figures—CRUNCH BERRIES (bk)
10", QUAKER OATS, 1969. $200 $300 $400

Cap'n Crunch wiggle figures
2.75"-3.25", QUAKER OATS, 1969. EA $25 $50 $75 [RC]

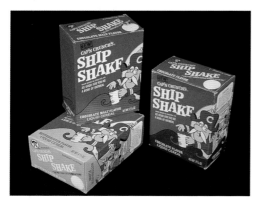

Three flavors CAP'N CRUNCH'S SHIP SHAKE
EA 5.75", QUAKER OATS, 1969-70.  EA $75 $125 $175

CAP'N CRUNCH'S SHIP SHAKE shaker
5.75", QUAKER OATS, 1969-70.  $15 $35 $60

Quisp laser-light—QUISP
10", QUAKER OATS, 1969.  $200 $450 $750

Quisp laser-light—QUISP (bk)
10", QUAKER OATS, 1969.  $200 $450 $750

Quisp laser-light (detail)
7". QUAKER OATS. 1969. $100 $175 $250 [AS]

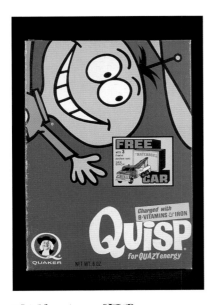

Matchbox toys—QUISP
10". QUAKER OATS. 1969. $150 $350 $500

Matchbox toys—QUISP & QUAKE (bks)
EA 10". QUAKER OATS. 1969.
$150-200 $350-450 $500-750

Matchbox toys (bush hat Quake)—QUAKE
10". QUAKER OATS. 1969. $200 $450 $750

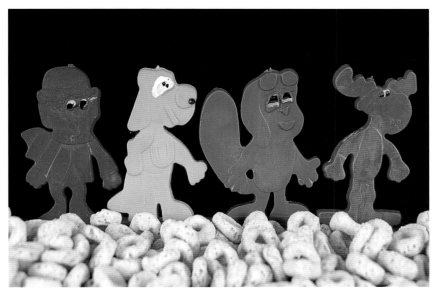

Rocky, Bullwinkle, Underdog, & Lucky Leprechaun springys
EA 2". GENERAL MILLS, 1969.  EA $10 $20 $35

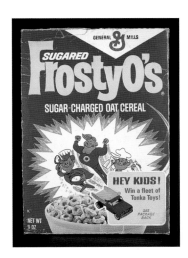

Tonka toy contest (Energy 3)—FROSTY Os
9.5". GENERAL MILLS, 1969.  $75 $150 $200

Trix rabbit rocket (spring fired)
3". GENERAL MILLS, 1969.  $10 $25 $50

Wacky Racer trio
2"-2.25" LONG, GENERAL MILLS, 1969.
EA $15 $45 $75 [BK/RC]

Bullwinkle breakfast set
PLATE 7.75" ACROSS, GENERAL MILLS, 1969-70.
SET $10 $25 $45

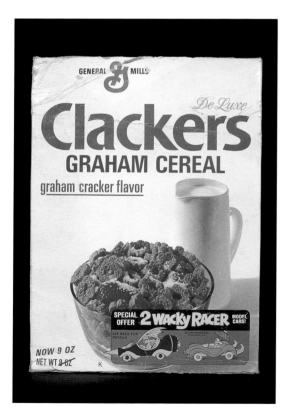

Wacky Racer model—CLACKERS
9.5", GENERAL MILLS, 1969.  $100 $225 $350

Wacky Racer model—CLACKERS (bk)
9.5", GENERAL MILLS, 1969.  $125 $250 $400

Mean Machine & Compact Pussycat models
6"-7" LONG. GENERAL MILLS. 1969. EA $100 $175 $250 [JB]

Quacker—CORN BURSTS
9.5". GENERAL MILLS. 1969. $100 $200 $300

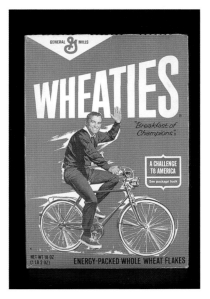

Bob Richards' "Challenge to America"—
WHEATIES
12.25". GENERAL MILLS. 1969. $45 $75 $100 [RS]

Archie offers—RAISIN BRAN & two TOASTIES
7.5"/9.5"/12", POST, 1969. $50-65 $75-100 $125-150

Archie offers—RAISIN BRAN & TOASTIES (bks)
7.5"/12", POST, 1969. $50-65 $75-100 $125-150

Archies rub-on button set
EA SHEET 5" X 6", POST, 1969. $25 $50 $75 [RC]

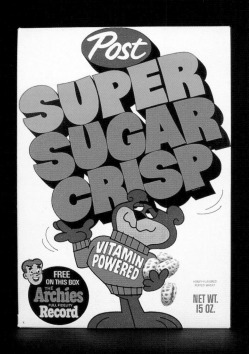

Archies on-pack record—SUPER SUGAR CRISP
10". POST. 1969.  $100 $125 $150

Archies on-pack record—SUPER SUGAR CRISP (bk)
10". POST. 1969.  $100 $125 $150

Archies cutout record & Jughead's hat
RECORD, POST, 1969. $3 $7 $10
HAT 6.5" ACROSS, POST, 1969. $25 $50 $75 [AS/AC]

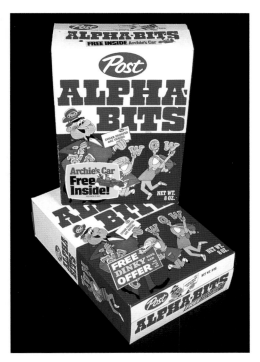

Archie's car & Dinky toys—ALPHA BITS
EA 8.5", POST, 1969.  $50-100 $100-175 $175-250

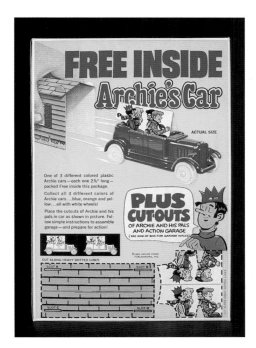

Archie's car—ALPHA BITS (bk)
8.5", POST, 1969.  $100 $175 $250

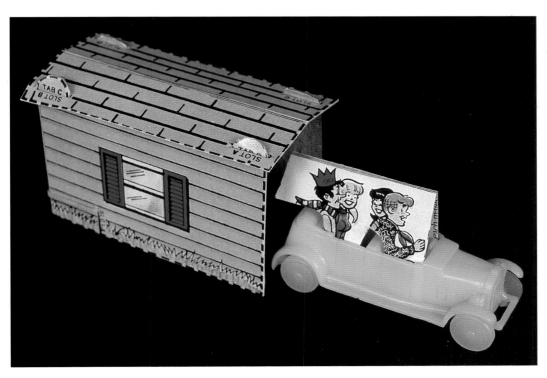

Archie's car & cutout garage
CAR 3" LONG. POST, 1969.  $10 $25 $35

Chitty Chitty Bang Bang helmet, goggles, bowl & mug—
TOASTIES & model car—HONEYCOMB
9.75"/9.5", POST, 1969.

Chitty Chitty Bang Bang model car (mock-up wing)
3" LONG, POST, 1969.  $5 $15 $25

Chitty Chitty Bang Bang model car—HONEYCOMB
(bk, mock-up wing)
9.5", POST, 1969.  $75 $125 $175

Chitty Chitty Bang Bang helmet,
goggles, bowl & mug—TOASTIES (bk)
9.75". POST, 1969. $75 $125 $175

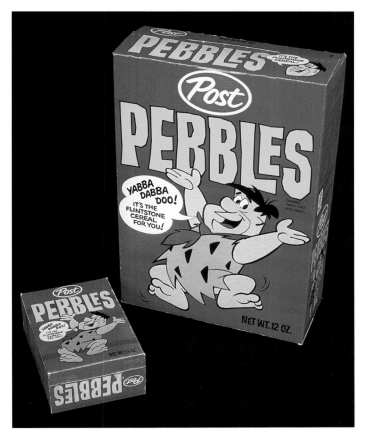

Sample & introductory (Fred Flintstone)—PEBBLES
4"/9". POST, 1969. $15-75 $35-125 $75-175

Chitty Chitty Bang Bang bowl & mug
BOWL 6" ACROSS, POST, 1969. SET $25 $60 $100

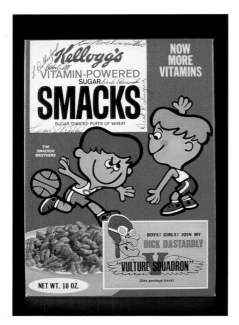

Vulture Squadron (Smackin' Bros.)—SUGAR SMACKS
(with printer signatures)
9", KELLOGG, 1969. $125 $200 $350

Vulture Squadron—SUGAR SMACKS
(bk, with printer signatures)
9", KELLOGG, 1969. $125 $200 $350

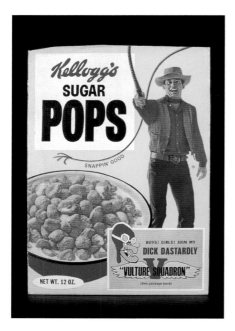

Vulture Squadron (Whippersnapper)—SUGAR POPS
10", KELLOGG, 1969. $100 $200 $300

Vulture Squadron flight kit
MAILER 9" X 12", KELLOGG, 1969. $150 $200 $250

Dick Dastardly squadron medals
EA 1.5" X 2.5". KELLOGG, 1969. EA $7 $15 $25

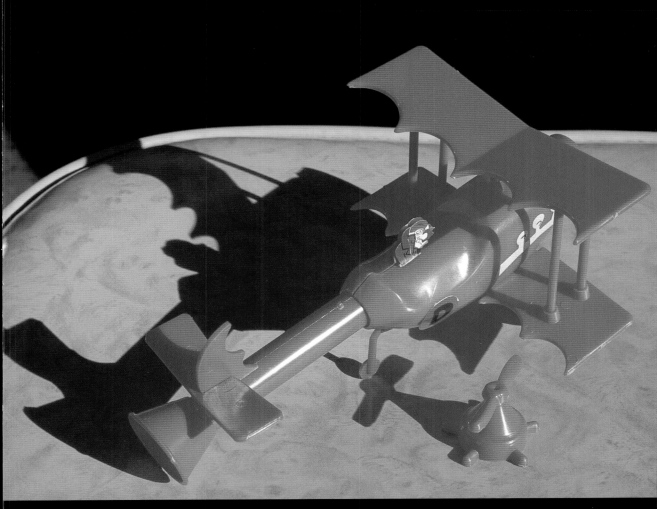

Dick Dastardly telescope plane

STRAWBERRY, CHOCOLATE, & ORANGE (Blue Gnu)–KOMBOs
EA 9". KELLOGG, 1969. EA $100 $200 $300

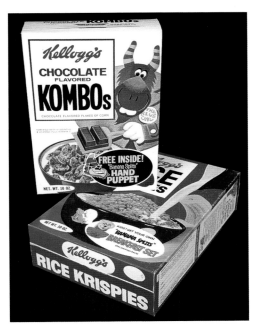

Splits hand puppets—KOMBOs & Splits breakfast set—
RICE KRISPIES
9"/10". KELLOGG. 1968. $100-150 $200-300 $300-450

Banana Splits hand puppets
EA 9". KELLOGG. 1968-69. EA $10 $20 $35

Banana Splits breakfast set—RICE KRISPIES (bk)
10". KELLOGG. 1969. $150 $300 $450

Fleegle mug & Banana Splits bowl
STACK 5.5". KELLOGG. 1969. SET $25 $75 $125 [AS]

Banana Splits posters (Moon man)—STARS
9", KELLOGG. 1969. $100 $200 $300

Banana Splits posters (Moon man)—STARS (bk)
9", KELLOGG. 1969. $100 $200 $300

Banana Splits pin-up posters—
PUFFA PUFFA RICE
9", KELLOGG. 1969. $100 $200 $300

Banana Splits poster (Drooper)
29" X 21". KELLOGG. 1969. EA $25 $50 $75 [BK]

Banana Splits stuffed toys
9"-10". KELLOGG. 1968. EA $15 $35 $50

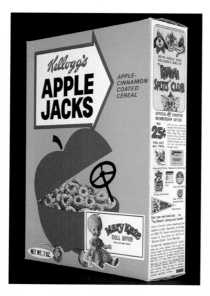

Banana Splits club (apple car)—APPLE JACKS
9". KELLOGG. 1969. $75 $125 $150

Crater Creatures—APPLE JACKS (bk panel)
8" X 6.5". KELLOGG. 1969. PANEL $15 $25 $45 [DG/SR]

Banana Splits club kit
MAILER 9" X 11.5". KELLOGG. 1969. $150 $200 $250 [AS]

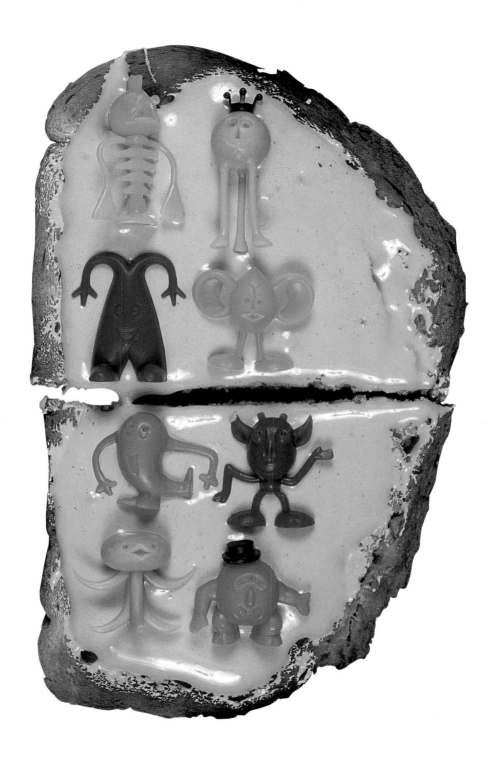

Crater Creatures set
1"-1.75". KELLOGG. 1969. EA $10-35 $20-50 $35-75 [AC/GT]

BOTTOM VIEW OF A FEW POPULAR CEREAL BOXES

The End